The Collieries of Northumberland

Volume I

James T. Tuck

Printed and Published by Trade Union Printing Services,
30 Lime Street, Newcastle upon Tyne NE1 2PQ.
Telephone 091-232 0990.

ISBN 1-871518-08-3

Dedicated to my late grandfather Thomas Tuck, a true Northumberland miner.

Foreword

By Dennis Murphy, Secretary of the Northumberland Mechanics' Association (NUM)

It gives me a great deal of pleasure to write the foreword to this book on the Northumberland collieries.

Northumberland forms half of the Great Northern Coalfield which stretches from Yorkshire to the Scottish Borders, taking in the counties of Durham and Northumberland.

When coal is discussed many people think of Durham, yet Northumberland has played a major part in mining history.

The first miners' union was formed by Thomas Hepburn in Northumberland. He was a man of great vision and united Durham and Northumberland miners in strike action against the coal owners. The first strikes of 1831 and 1832 were not successful, but he realised times would change, saying:

'If we have not been successful, at least we as a body of miners have been able to bring our grievances before the public, and the time will come when the Golden Chains which bind the tyrants together will be snapped, and men will be properly organised when coal owners will be like ordinary men and will have to sigh for the days gone by. It only needs time to bring this about.' How right he was.

The miners of Northumberland sent the first Miners' MP, Thomas Burt, to parliament. The Northumberland Miners' Union, in recognition of his services to the miners, named after him their offices built in the centre of Newcastle.

Our Mining Committees, through miners' contributions, built schools, hospitals and libraries long before the welfare state. The formation of the Northumberland Aged Mineworkers' Homes Association was another visionary move. Nearly 600 cottages were built and let free of charge to retired mineworkers; they still provide much needed accommodation today.

Whilst coal has been mined for nearly

Dennis Murphy

600 years in Northumberland, very few books have been written to document our rich history. This book seeks to record by pictures and a number of facts the collieries that were nationalised in 1947. Nationalisation was a dream fulfilled for a generation of people who had worked and lobbied to bring it about. The principle was established but a tremendous amount of work was still to be done. The pits had been virtually unchanged since the turn of the century. Investment was slow in coming and when it did many pits were closed.

The 1950s and 1960s was a period of industrial turmoil. Northumberland miners moved to the Midlands coalfields to start new lives away from their families and friends.

The decline in the industry continues today. In 1993 the mining industry is on the verge of complete closure. Northumberland has one remaining coal mine, Ellington.

It is fitting that this book should be published while mining continues. It is most important to record and document such an important part of the region's economy and heritage.

I hope the reader enjoys it as much as I have. It will be an important reference work, for I'm sure this era of mining will attract much attention from future generations.

Dennis Murphy,
General Secretary, Northumberland Mechanics, Blyth, 1993.

Preface

One spring afternoon in 1984 my six-year-old daughter returned from school with a request that I help her with her history project. Could I, she enquired, get her some photographs of the local pits?

I had no way of knowing that this gentle appeal was to become what my family and friends have come to regard as my obsession with the history of the Northumberland coalfield.

It is all the more surprising that my interests have developed in this way when I recall that my days down the pit were suffered with the minimum of enthusiasm, a fact that was the subject of many an overman's scathing rebuke.

However it is now ten years since I started to help my daughter with her project. Her interests are now those of a happy well- adjusted teenager, and while her project is not entirely forgotten it does not hold for her the fascination that it once did. I, on the other hand, have spent ten years crawling through the overgrown sites of long-abandoned pits, and sitting for hours poring over the archives of the County Records Office and of the Mining Institute. When I was not doing this I was travelling the County begging for photographs.

I have pestered many kind and unsuspecting ex-miners for their recollections and will always be grateful for the memories they have shared with me.

I have received help from many quarters where I would have least expected help, and have on some occasions been a little discouraged by those from whom I could reasonably have expected more help; discouraged because I feel that history is for sharing, not for hoarding as if it was the property of an individual.

This book is essentially one man's view of the coalfield. It is not the definitive history or the last word. Some statements have the authority of documentation, others are the memories of men and women of the coalfield.

My hope is that this book will be a stimulus to the people of Northumberland to come forward and to say, 'He hasn't got that right. I have an old map that contra-

James T. Tuck

dicts that statement', or, 'I have a better photograph than that one'.

This way we will be able to build on this book and develop a more comprehensive knowledge of our history.

Ellington Colliery is now the last colliery in the County. If the present climate continues that may soon be gone and an industry will be dead that, at the time of nationalisation, once supported 70 collieries and 30,000 miners and their families in Northumberland.

The innovation and skill, involved in sinking the mines of Northumberland, and the hardship and occasional joys of the miners who worked those dangerous seams must not be forgotten. The next generations will be the poorer if it is, for what future do they have if our past is so easily cast aside?

I hope that this book will play some role in preserving our heritage.

James T. Tuck,
October 1993.

Acknowledgements

Compiling this volume has been no easy task for me and I owe a debt of gratitude to many people. The number is so great that I will not be able to mention them all by name, so to those whose names I have missed I apologize.

Where a photograph has been donated the name of the donor has been printed below the photograph. Many thanks to them all. Where there is no accreditation, the photograph is from my personal collection.

I would like to thank Dave Temple, a Durham miner, for editing this book and making its publication possible; my father for his support; Jim Lawson of the Beamish Museum, and the Museum itself; all the staff at the County Records Offices in Melton Park and Morpeth for their help; Dennis Murphy for his foreword; and Dr Stafford Lyndsey for his time and books. A special thanks to Mick Tosney of Blyth for all his efforts. For their great help on the history of Longhirst Drift, thanks to Kit Miller, the pit's last manager, and Bob English of Linton. Likewise, Mr Jack Nathan, the last secretary of NACODS at Eccles Colliery, for his help on the history of the Backworth Collieries, and many thanks to Derek Charlton of Newcastle.

I must thank several local newspapers for their help with my appeals: the Berwick Advertiser, the Hexham Courant, the News Post Group of Papers, the Morpeth Herald, Evening Chronicle, and Coal News. Thanks to the staff of the North of England Mining Institute, especially Barbara; Alan Hill of Birmingham for his advice and help; Alan Oliver of Holystone and Peter Martin of Blaydon for their tireless efforts; last but not least, my wife and daughter for just being there.

Appeal

Many of the photographs in this book are of exceptional quality. Some you may think are no more than drawings, but remember as our history vanishes so do many of the photographs. How many times after something has gone do we think, 'I wish I had photographed that', or 'Somebody must have a photograph of that, it stood for years'?. Sadly this is the case with some of the collieries of Northumberland. A combination of big shifts in population, the older generation passing on and their artefacts disposed of, not always kindly, means it is not always possible to acquire a photograph at all, let alone one of good quality. In some cases, at the present time, none exist, which is the reason for this appeal.

If you have any photographs of the Northumberland collieries and the life of its miners and their families they will be welcome, and particularly ones relating to: Acomb, Callerton Drift, Gloria, Hedley Park, Morwood, Lambley or any of the Naworth Group, Stagshaw Bank, West Clifton, Venters Hall and Throckley Coronation.

I feel this is so important that I am asking any reader who can help to please contact me by telephone on Blyth 363808. This may be our last chance to have a photographic record of a once great industry.

James T. Tuck

Contents

History

The collieries described in this book were working collieries in Northumberland on Vesting Day 1947, when the coal industry was nationalised.

To fully appreciate the historical context in which these pits were developed and later declined, it is useful to sketch out a few of the milestones in the history of the Northumberland Coalfield and the men who worked its mines.

No one knows the exact date when the first coal was won from shallow drifts where the coal measures outcropped, or from the scores of primitive bell pits[1] that littered the County, but mining proper in the form of shafts and underground workings dates from around 1620. These mines had shafts, pumps and some form of rudimentary ventilation, which allowed the workings to extend several hundred yards from the shaft.

The frequency of new sinkings in the County mirrored the pace of Britain's emerging Industrial Revolution. The shafts became deeper and their workings more extensive.

By 1700 the first recorded disaster took place at Bensham Colliery, Gateshead, where 80 lives were lost when, on the first attempt to work the Low Main seam, a gas explosion occurred.

The 18th century brought greater demands for coal as the pace of industrialisation accelerated, and as the mines deepened in the search for the more productive coal measures the need for innovation increased.

Newcomen engine at work in late 1880s
Photograph Peter Martin, Blaydon

Newcomen steam engines were developed to pump water out of the mines and, in 1763, Joseph Oxley adapted one of these engines to power a winding engine, for drawing coal at Hartly Colliery.

The harsh and cruel conditions endured

by the miners of these days was to cause the first recorded miners' strike in 1765.

In 1768 James Watt built his famous steam engine. Although historians, at least those who write school text books, have given Watt the credit for first harnessing the power of steam, it is a fact that Watt observed Joseph Oxley's engine at work prior to building his own version. However, by 1784 Watt's engine was installed and working at Walker Colliery, a colliery that 10 years later would introduce cast iron tubing.

Towards the end of the 18th century, in 1797, at Benwell Colliery the first self-acting incline was in operation.

Gosforth Colliery from a drawing by T.H. Hair

The 19th century brought more advances in the use of machinery and sadly more disasters.

In 1812 a young colliery mechanic at Killingworth Colliery called George Stephenson invented the first underground haulage engine. Two years later he would give 'Blucher', his first steam engine, its trial run.

In 1815 Heaton Colliery was inundated with water with the loss of 90 lives. The relentless expansion of the coalfield continued, the rich profits to be had encouraging greater feats of engineering.

In 1829 Gosforth Colliery was sunk to a depth of 1,100 feet through the 90 fathom dyke.

In 1831 Thomas Hepburn formed the first miners' Union of Northumberland and Durham and that year led a successful strike, which won a 12-hour working day for children instead of extremely long hours.

In 1832, in an effort to still better their conditions, the miners struck again. This time the combined forces of masters and military defeated the miners and the Union was smashed.

In 1834 the first iron tubs were introduced to Northumberland's mines. One year later, disaster struck the Wallsend Colliery when a terrible explosion killed 102 men and boys.

In 1836 the detached safety hook was invented and was gradually introduced. This invention prevented cages being pulled over the pulley wheels, an ever present hazard of the times. In 1844, having recovered from the defeat of 1832, the pitmen

A Walker indestructible fan Photograph A. Hill, Birmingham

formed a new Union and struck against the harsh terms of the 'bond'[2].

In 1847 the Mines and Collieries Bill was introduced to parliament seeking to appoint Government inspectors of mines and legislate for higher safety standards. It was withdrawn the same year under pressure from the coal owners.

The 1850s was again a period of struggle for better conditions, with miners appealing to parliament for legislation compelling the owners to introduce safety measures.

Then in 1862, on 6th January, that terrible day, the beam of the pumping engine at Hartley Colliery snapped and fell into its only shaft, caving it in and trapping 204 men and boys without ventilation. For six days they laboured to free the trapped men, but to no avail. Only one man, fortunate enough to be in the cage at the time the beam came crashing down the shaft,

New Hartley Colliery Hester Pit, 1862, after the disaster.

The state coach to the right of this picture tends to suggest that the photograph was taken at the start of the funeral procession for the victims of the disaster. The two men in top hats almost certainly are Carr, the owner of the mine, and George Baker Forster, the man who led the attempted rescue.

Photograph Norman Whitelock, Holystone

survived. Legislation was now passed compelling all owners to ensure that every new mine had two means of escape and, from 1st January 1865, that every existing mine had a second means of escape.

After well over 200 years of mining, after great strides had been made in the harnessing of machinery to produce greater and greater quantities of coal, it had taken a disaster of these proportions to establish the simple right of the men who produced the coal to have a second means of escape. Time has not diminished the anger miners still feel when reminded of this waste of human life.

The latter part of the 1800s saw a new phase in the development of the Northumberland coalfield. Coal mining was more and more becoming a target for the inward investment of capital, with the formation of powerful coal companies having the ability to finance the sinking of deeper shafts through the carboniferous limestone to reach the lower coal measures.

Despite the cyclical rise and fall in the world demand for coal, the latter half of the 19th century and the first decade of the 20th century were years of growth for the County's coal industry.

The Northumberland coalfield was principally an exporting coalfield and was, therefore, more susceptible to the unpredictable swings of world trade than other coalfields that serviced the more stable home market.

This was to prove the source of many disputes between the miners and the owners as the latter sought to reduce

Walker Colliery a hundred years after Watt's engine was installed

the cost of labour when world prices took a dive. Such was the tension caused that an attempt was made, with the agreement of the miners' Union, to tie the wages of the men to the selling price of coal on a sliding scale of wages.

Coal production in the County hit its peak in 1913. From this date it was to decline, slowly at first, passing through periods of reprieve as the demands of wars and the brief upturns in world trade dictated, but nevertheless always declining. This is not to say that no new sinkings were made after 1913, but that more capacity closed down than was created.

In 1925 new legislation was to follow the disaster at the Montague View Pit in Newcastle, where 38 men and boys were killed when the mine was inundated with water. This legislation compelled mine owners to file their mining plans with the local council. Once again it had taken a disaster to bring about a legal remedy to the chaotic development of the country's mines.

The 20th century saw a big change in the management of the coal industry in general. So anarchic had the production of coal become that the Liberal Government was forced to put the mines under Government control for the whole period of the First World War.

In 1921 the famous Sankey Commission sat with representatives of Union, industry and coal owners. The result of their deliberations was to recommend that the country's mines be taken into public own-

Pit head baths Photo J. Law Collection

ership. Only the coal owners rejected this report. It was not, however, until 1st January 1947, Vesting Day, that the mines were finally nationalised.

Nationalisation brought new investment to the mines and with it rationalisation. Once the post-war fuel crisis had subsided in the mid-1950s, the NCB sought to reduce capacity and close mines.

It started gradually, but as the river of cheap oil flowing into the country became a flood so the pit closure programme of the 1960s decimated the coal mines of the County of Northumberland.

Miners were to complain that while nationalisation had brought many benefits, in safety standards and such luxuries as pit-head baths, little on the management side had changed. All the miners' co-operation and goodwill was rewarded by making them one of the poorest-paid workforces by 1972.

This was to be redressed to some degree by the wages strikes of 1972 and 1974. The unthinkable had happened, while the country was still heavily dependent on coal for power the oil-producing countries trebled the price of oil, putting the miners in a powerful bargaining position.

Having squandered the miners' goodwill in the post-war period, a deal was done and a 'Plan for Coal' was introduced. For nearly a decade the pace of closures was almost halted.

The recent history is well known and we do not have to elaborate it here. The year-long, bitter strike of 1984-85 and ten years of campaigning to keep pits open has not changed the mind of the Government.

It is now a subject of speculation as to whether this book sketching the history of 25 of the mines working at the time of nationalisation will appear in print before the last pit in this once-great coalfield is closed.

Notes

1 Bell pits were short shafts where coal was taken to the limits of primitive ventilation, and were probably first sunk in the Middle Ages.

2 The bond was the unequal agreement signed once a year that bound the miner to the pit by law for the course of the next 12 months. Miners were frequently taken to court and imprisoned for breaking the conditions of the bond.

Seams of the Northumberland Coalfield

N.C.B. NAME	WYLAM & MONTAGU	SEGHILL & WALLSEND	STOBSWOOS & ASHINGTON	HAUXLEY & BROOMHILL	TYNEDALE
1. SEAM D. HIGH MAIN	——	MOORLAND	BLACKCLOSE ASHINGTON	BLACKCLOSE	——
2. MARINE BAND	——	——	HIGH MAIN D/E	UNNAMED	——
3. HIGH MAIN E.	MAIN OR KENTON MAIN	HIGH MAIN	< HIGH MAIN E1 DIAMOND G2	UNNAMED	——
4. MAIN F.	MAIN OR NEWBIGGIN STONE	< METAL F1 STONE F2	< MIDDLE MAIN F1 BOTTOM MAIN F2	RADCLIFFE	——
5. Yard G	YARD	< TOP YARD G1 OR BLAKE BOTTOM YARD G2	< BENTICK G1 YARD G2	ALBERT	——
6. MAUDLIN H	BENSHAM OR GLOVE	BENSHAM	< TOP BENSHAM H1 BOTTOM BENSHAM H2	< QUEEN H1 LITTLE WONDER H2	—— ——
7. LOW MAIN J	HUTTON (WYLAM ONLY)	< SIX QUARTER J1 FIVE QUARTER J1	FIVE QUARTER	——	GRAND LEASE MAIN
8. BRASS THILL K	< LOW MAIN OR BENWELL MAIN BOTTOM LOW MAIN (WYLAM ONLY)	< FIVE QUARTER K1 LOE MAIN K2	LOW MAIN	< TOP OR PRINCESS K1 MAIN OR DUKE K2	CROW
9. HUTTON L	RULER	PLESSEY	PLESSEY	BOTTOM COAL	CANDLE
10. PLESSEY M.		BOTTOM YARD	CHEEVELEY OR BOTTOM PLESSEY	CHEEVELEY	OLD 5/4 OR GLOVE
11. HARVEY N.	BEAUMONT ENGINE OR TOWNELEY	BEAUMONT OR ENGINE	BEAUMONT	BEAUMONT	——
12. HODGE O	HODGE	HODGE	STOBSWOOD TILLEY OR OR HODGE	——	——
13. TILLEY P	TILLEY	DENTON LOW MAIN	WIDDRINGTON YARD OR TILLEY	GIVENS OR WIDDRINGTON YARD	BOUNDER
14. BUSTY Q	< STONE OR FIVE QUARTER G1 FIVE QUARTER G2 OR SIX QUOARTER	TOP BUSTY Q1 BOTTOM BUSTY Q2	PEGSWOOD HARVEY OR TOP BUSTY PEGSWOOD BOTTOM BUSTY OR BOTTOM BUSTY	WIDDRINGTON FIVE QUARTER WIDDRINGTON TOP MAIN	UPPER GRAIG NOOK LOWER GRAIG NOOK
15. THREE QUARTER R	THREE QUARTER OR YARD	THREE QUARTER	PEGSWOOD BOTTOM BUSTY OR THREE QUARTER	WIDDRINGTON BOTTOM MAIN	LITTLE
16. BROCKWELLS	DENTON LOW MAIN OR BROCKWELL	BROCKWELL OR BANDY	< BANDY BROCKWELL	BANDY	< HALF WELLSYKE OR COOM ROOF
17. VICTORIA T.	VICTORIA	VICTORIA	CHOPPINGTON BROCKWELL	CHOPPINGTON VICTORIA	< HIGH MAIN SLAG OR SEVEN QUARTER
18. MARSHALL GREEN U	MARSHALL GREEN OR HORSLEY WOOD	MARSHALL GREEN	CHOPPINGTON VICTORIA	——	< SEVEN QUARTER LOW MAIN
19. CANISTER CLAY V	NEVER WORKED IN EAST OF THE COUNTY				< LOW MAIN STRINGER

SEAMS A. B. AND C. ONLY APPEAR IN DURHAM WHERE < APPEARS IT MEANS THE SEAM SPLITS INTO TWO AND —— MEANS SEAM UNWORKABLE OR NOT THERE.

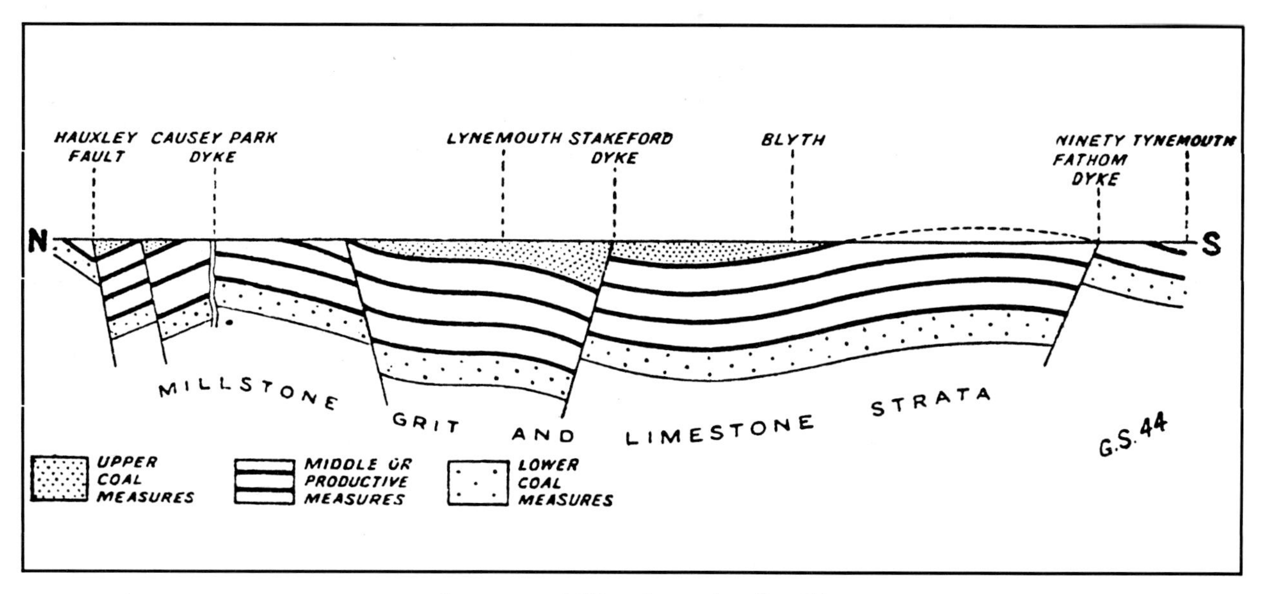

Strata of Northumberland

In discussing the seams of any coalfield it has to be remembered that coal mining is an inexact science, the mining engineer having no accurate map of where the coal measures and the faults lie. Information is gained from a relatively small number of test bores, which give an accurate indication of where the coal measures lie only at that particular point.

The exact path of a fault or a seam is plotted between proven positions by a mixture of guess work and experience. Only when a seam is worked is its position proven without doubt. A coal seam can often disappear, having been thrown upward by the massive tensions developed in the earth's crust millions of years ago. On some occasions the seam will split into two separate seams. In other places it will disappear without trace into what miners call a washout.

The Northumberland coalfield is part of the great North Coalfield that stretches from the south of County Durham to the north of Northumberland and from the Pennine Hills in the west out to under the North Sea.

The part of this coalfield that lies within the boundaries of Northumberland is split into three parts by a massive intrusion of hard ignious rock, formed millions of years ago when molten rock was forced into great cracks in the earth's crust.

This intrusion is known as the Whinsill Dyke and runs from the Kyloe Hills north of Berwick, sweeps over towards the Farne Isles, before continuing south, then turning west it cuts across the north side of Newcastle and on into Cumbria, where it ends near Brampton.

Where the great glaciers of the Ice Age left this volcanic rock exposed, it became a useful natural line of fortification for all those who sought to defend the area from the Scots. The Roman general Hadrian built his wall along its length at Housteads. Bamburgh Castle and the castle on Holy Island all rest on this hard and impervious rock.

A comfort to the defenders of Northumberland, to the miners it was a great barrier, dangerous and impenetrable.

To the north of the Dyke are the Scremerson Coal Measures, which are generally of low-quality coal providing only six workable seams. This is a part of the coalfield where coal working started in the reign of Queen Elizabeth I. By the time of nationalisation only one mine was working these seams.

To the west lie the Tynedale Measures in the Limestone series. Here there are 12 workable seams of mixed quality. The vast majority of these seams exist in an area around Coanwood on the border of Cumberland, with only two or three seams existing throughout the area. In 1947 the district supported seven working mines.

The eastern sector of the coalfield was by far the largest and most important. Here the coal lies between layers of carboniferous limestone and sandstone. There are 24 seams in all and they were formed at a much earlier period than those in the middle and upper limestone series.

The naming of the seams is complicated and unpredictable. Some seams, for instance the Plessey, were named after the family of coal owners who first worked the seams. Others, like the Beaumont, after the person who discovered their existence.

Beaumont was a mining engineer who invented the bore rods that were first used to probe for the hidden seams. In 1620 he arrived in Northumberland a wealthy man with £20,000 to his name, and died a pauper in a Nottingham jail.

Other seams were named after their particular characteristics. The Yard seam because it is barely a yard thick at its thickest. The Brass Thill is so called because of its hard roof; Brass Thill meaning just that. Some took the name of the place where they outcrop, such as the Bensham.

Some seams were called different names at different collieries causing confusion.

In an attempt to end the confusion, the NCB gave official names to all the seams giving them a letter or a number and in some cases a name[1]. Unfortunately miners being miners often continued to call the seams by their old names. In many cases the confusion persisted.

1 In this book where the seams of the coalfield are stated the NCB name will be used with the local name in brackets. All manpower and tonnage figures are those of the NCB, unless otherwise stated.

The Northumberland Collieries

This list shows the 70 working units in the NCB grouping.

1. Acomb
2. Algernon
3. Ashington
4. Bardon Mill
5. Barmoor
6. Bates
7. Bedlington A
8. Bedlington D
9. Bedlington E
10. Bedlington F
11. Blackhill
12. Brenkley
13. Broomhill
14. Burradon
15. Callerton
16. Callerton Drift
17. Cambois
18. Choppington A
19. Choppington B
20. Crofton Mill
21. Dinnington
22. Dudley
23. East Walbottle
24. Eccles
25. Ellington
26. Fenwick
27. Gloria
28. Hartford
29. Hauxley
30. Havannah
31. Hazlerigg
32. Horton Grange
33. Isabella-Cowpen
34. Lambley
35. Linton
36. Longhirst
37. Loughbridge
38. Lynemouth
39. Maude
40. Montague
41. Morwood
42. Naworth
43. Nelson
44. Netherton
45. Newbiggin
46. New Delaval
47. New Hartley
48. North Seaton
49. North Walbottle
50. Pegswood
51. Prestwick
52. Rake Lane
53. Rising Sun-Wallsend
54. Seaton Burn
55. Seaton Delaval
56. Seghill
57. Shilbottle
58. Stagshaw Bank
59. Stobswood
60. Throckley Blucher
61. Throckley Coronation
62. Throckley Isabella
63. Throckley Maria
64. Ventners Hall
65. Weetslade
66. West Clifton
67. Whittle
68. West Wylam
69. Williams
70. Woodhorn

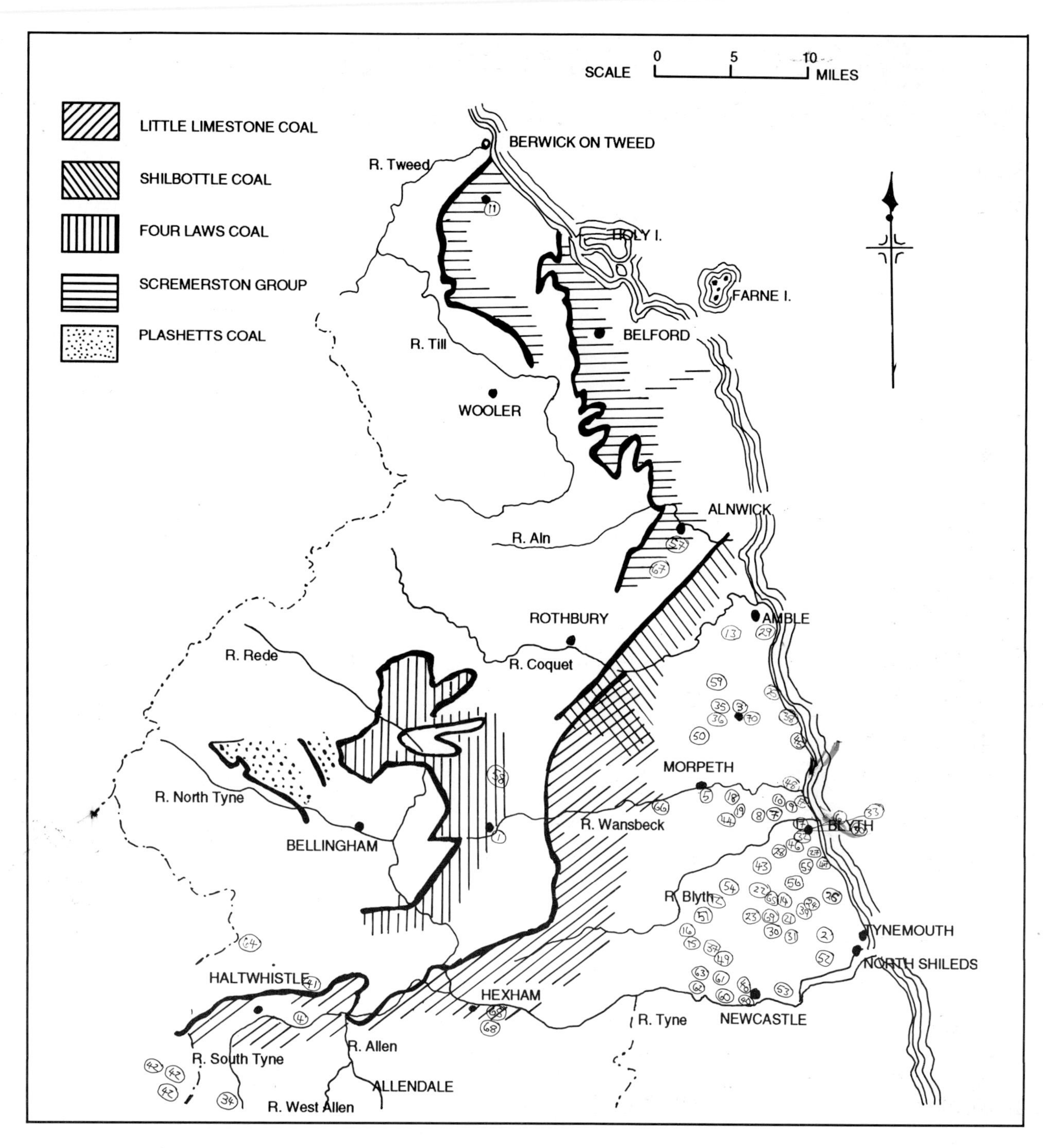
SCALE
0
5
10
MILES
LITTLE LIMESTONE COAL
SHILBOTTLE COAL
FOUR LAWS COAL
SCREMERSTON GROUP
PLASHETTS COAL
BERWICK ON TWEED
R. Tweed
HOLY I.
FARNE I.
BELFORD
R. Till
WOOLER
ALNWICK
R. Aln
AMBLE
ROTHBURY
R. Rede
R. Coquet
MORPETH
R. North Tyne
R. Wansbeck
BLYTH
BELLINGHAM
R Blyth
TYNEMOUTH
NORTH SHILEDS
HALTWHISTLE
HEXHAM
R. Tyne
NEWCASTLE
R. Allen
R. South Tyne
ALLENDALE
R. West Allen

Left: Tail gate of Long Wall face

Below: Miner drawing timber from goaf of long wall — an early armoured conveyor is in foreground

Mining terms and methods

The language of mining is so old and complicated that when combined with the Northumberland dialect it constitutes a language in its own right. Such words as ‘Chum’ meaning empty and ‘Kist’ meaning a box or chest owe their origin to the old Norse invaders.

The task of explaining these terms is made the more difficult because they vary not just between regions but from pit to pit.

Here we attempt to explain only some of the terms used in this book to help those with no experience of mining.

Boy attaching tubs to endless hauler, 1924 Photograph John Reed, Bedlington

Bank: Surface.

Banksman: The surface worker who dispatches men and materials into the cage.

Cage: The steel structure that carries men and materials down the shaft.

Drift: An underground roadway driven at a gradient either from surface underground or between levels underground. A mine that has no vertical shafts is known as a drift mine.

Endless Haulage: A common method of transport where a tub or mine-car is attached to an 'endless' steel rope. This rope is wrapped around the drum of an engine, which provides the motive force at one end, and a return wheel at the other. The direction of the engine can be reversed to take the tubs or 'sets' in-bye or out-bye.

Heapstead: The structure above and around the shaft at the surface.

Inset: A facility made in a shaft where coals can be loaded into a skip at a place other than the shaft bottom.

In-bye: Towards the coal face. (Out-bye means away from the coal face.)

Laid in: When a shaft falls into disuse and its structures are dismantled.

Main and Tail Haulage: This method of haulage differs from the endless method in that the driving engine has two drums and two ropes, the main being attached to the out-bye end of the set while the tail rope is taken round the return wheel and attached to the in-bye end of the set. The two drums of the haulage engine turn in opposite directions. While one is hauling the other is taking up the slack.

Royalty: The area of coal for which the mine owners held the mining rights.

Staple shaft: An underground shaft between two seams.

Staithes: The docks where coal is loaded on to ships

The Take: The area of coal allotted to a colliery by the NCB.

The Vend: The ratio of saleable coal to the waste produced by a mine.

A Wash out: When a seam of coal is absent from a particular area.

Methods of extraction

Board and Pillar: This method of mining is known as partial extraction. Roadways or boards are driven in a regular lattice-work leaving pillars of coal between the boards to support the roof. In some cases when an area of the mine is being abandoned and there is no reason to leave the pillars, the pillars are also extracted, starting in-bye and working out.

The board-and-pillar method can also be worked in a herringbone construction. This consists of driving a central roadway, then driving boards on either side of the roadway and at an angle to it forming a herringbone pattern.

Long Wall: This is known as total extraction. In this method two roadways or gates are driven a fixed distance apart, usually

Coal cutter undercutting coal, 1936

Photograph Norman Bell, Blyth

either 100, 200 or 250 yards depending upon the roof conditions or the existence of faults.

If the face is to be an advancing face then the seam between the two roadways is extracted as the the roadways or gates are advanced. The face is ventilated by the passage of air down the main gate along the coal face and out of the tail gate. The main gate is sometimes known as the mother gate probably because it feeds the face.

In later years the retreating method of long wall mining became very popular. Here the main and tail gate would be pre-driven up to and some times beyond a 1,000 yards. The coal was then extracted from the in-bye end working out-bye. The gates collapsing as the face retreated.

The area where the coal has been extracted is known as the goaf.

The methods of winning coal are as diverse as are the degrees of thickness, hardness, quality and roof conditions of the coal seams themselves. In some seams the coal will yield itself without a struggle, in others it is so hard that miners describe it as bell metal. The pick and shovel survived in some mines for a surprisingly long time, and is still employed to this day in some private drifts.

The windy pick, a pneumatic hand-held tool, is a miniature version of that used to dig up roads. It superseded the pick and to this day is still an invaluable tool for the miner.

Since the turn of the century some form of mechanisation has been used in most

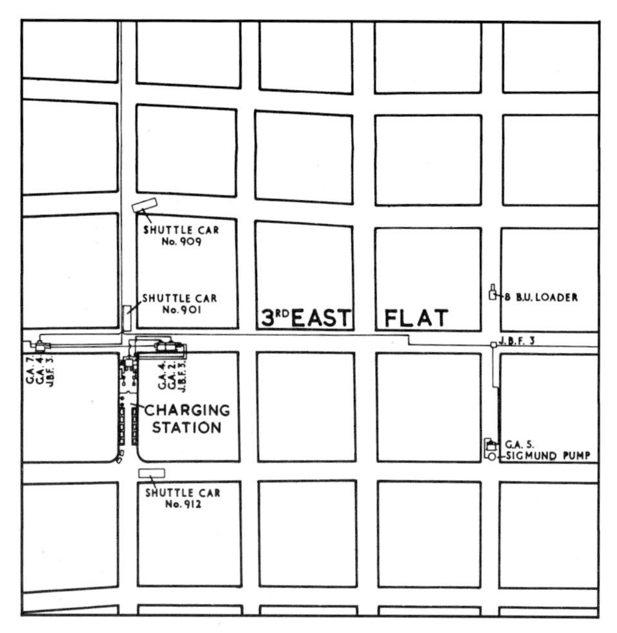

Plan of board-and-pillar workings, Weetslade Colliery 1951

mines that sought to produce large quantities of coal. The most common method was the use of coal cutters to undermine the coal. A narrow band of coal is cut usually at the bottom of the seam. The coal face is then drilled along its length. These drill holes are then filled with explosives by a deputy or a shotfirer and stemmed or sealed with clay or, in later years, a silicon gel.

The shots (explosives) will then be fired (detonated) and the coal will break up. Undercutting the coal ensures that the seam collapses vertically and prevents the coal being blown into the goaf. The coal can then be hand-filled on to the face-belt and transported to the main gate and out-bye.

Before the next round of production can start the face must be timbered and then the old timber drawn out, collapsing the roof and thus relieving the roof pressure on the face.

Although this method persisted in some collieries as late as the 1970s it started to be superseded after nationalisation, when armoured face conveyors and shearers were introduced.

The armoured face conveyor (AFC) is sometimes referred to by miners as 'pans', a shortened version of the German word 'panzer'. The early AFCs were of German design and panzer means armoured.

The AFC is a type of steel trough in which run two moving parallel chains connected by steel bars known as flight bars. The shearer is hauled up and down the face on top of the AFC. The method of haulage is dependent on the design of the shearer. The early shearers were dragged up the face on a chain connected to a hauler in the main gate, but the more common method is some form of integral haulage. In the integral haulage method the shearer pulls itself along a stationary chain or a toothed track on the AFC.

The shearer has at least one rotating drum fitted with a spiral of tungsten-tipped picks. These drums rotate in the seam of coal, tearing the coal out and throwing it on to the face conveyor. The constant moving of the flight bars under the coal moves it along the face to the main gate.

Other terms

Deputy: Underground foreman certified to fire shots.
NCB: National Coal Board.
BC: British Coal.

Ashington Colliery

The town of Ashington was once described as the biggest pit village in the world, owing to its distinctive long rows of pit houses built around the various shafts that constituted the Ashington mine. The earliest recorded sinking of a shaft in the area is that of the Portland and West Hartly Colliery (map reference 81NZ258879), between Pegswood and Ashington. This was its official name but it was always known locally as the 'Fell 'em Doon Pit'.

The adoption of the name Hartly appears to have been an attempt to cash in on the reputation for quality that the public associated with this name.

Ashington Colliery proper started in 1867, with the sinking of the Bothal Coal Shaft to the Grey Seam (or the Main Coal

Ashington Colliery in 1908

Men descending Duke Shaft

New Moor Shaft

as it was known locally) at a depth of 216 feet. This shaft was sunk half a mile north west of the town centre (map ref 81NZ265881).

From this small beginning was to grow one of the biggest mines in the world, and with it the famous Ashington Coal Company, with its advanced ideas on the safety and welfare of its workforce and the use of modern mining techniques.

The second shaft to be sunk was the Carl in 1873 to the Low Main seam, at a depth of 528ft. Such was the success of the Carl shaft that the owners sunk a third shaft, the Duke, in 1885 to the same depth and seam. It is possible that a fault separated the two shafts.

Each shaft had its own ventilation shaft making six shafts in all.

The Duke Upcast Shaft became a pumping shaft almost immediately after sinking.

The Bothal and Carl Upcast Shafts started their lives as furnace shafts, but some time between 1918 and 1921 the Carl became the main upcast shaft for the entire mine and was fitted with an electric fan and headgear for man-riding purposes. The Bothal Upcast Shaft had fallen into disuse by this time.

Not content with a six-shaft colliery, the owners set about the sinking of a seventh shaft, the New Moor, one mile north west of Ashington (map ref. 81 NZ 265895). The purpose of this shaft was to reduce the travelling time from shaft to face in the shallower coal measures.

The New Moor Shaft and its sister shaft, the Old Moor — which was part of Linton

Colliery — were unusual in that they were both fitted with Koepe winders and were used purely for man-riding purposes. The Koepe winder was the invention of a German mining engineer, Dr Koepe, and its distinguishing feature was that the electric motor was positioned above the shaft.

In 1924 the first drift, the Connygarth, was driven at the mine about a mile to the west and close to the site of the original 'Fell 'em Doon' mine (map ref. 81NZ242876).

Later a second drift, the Bothal Barns Drift, was driven approximately two-and-a-half miles south west of the colliery, on the outskirts of the village of Bothal.

While the Connygarth Drift was a coal-drawing drift, the Bothal Barns was used purely for the purposes of man-riding.

1934 saw the closure of the Bothal Barns Drift, though it had stood unused for many years.

The Connygarth Drift also closed; while it has not proved possible to find a record of the exact date of closure, local memory suggests 1930. The NCB reopened the drift in the 1950s.

By the time of nationalisation in 1947 the Ashington mine was a well-run, highly mechanised mine with electric locomotives underground and 90 per cent of its coal being machine-cut. It boasted a well-equipped training gallery, where generations of miners were prepared for the rigours of underground life.

Ashington Colliery continued to be a major force under the management of the NCB until 1964, when, in line with the general decline in the demand for coal, the Board began to streamline and run down the Ashington and Woodhorn Collieries.

The Tippler House, Ashington Colliery 1937

Photograph Norman Bell, Blyth

Duke Shaft on Vesting Day — note the NCB flag flying

First, the old coal washery was modified to make it more efficient and to cut down on manpower.

A third and final drift, the Bothal, was driven 150 yards from the shafts, linking up with Woodhorn underground. By 1966 this drift was complete and was drawing all the coal for the Ashington and Woodhorn Collieries. This new facility made the coal-drawing shafts of the complex redundant. The Duke, which had not

Ashington Training Gallery

drawn coal for some time, was immediately demolished. The Carl was used for materials and the upcast shaft remained for ventilation and man riding.

The Bothal, the Carl and the Upcast were to stand until the day the mine was finally closed, although the ropes were cut on the Bothal Shaft and the pulley wheels removed in the early 1970s.

The Conneygarth Drift suffered the same fate as the coal shafts and closed in 1966, its reserves being worked via the Bothal Drift.

By the late 1960s the streamlining of the mine was completed with the closure of the New Moor shaft. From this point the Colliery would suffer a gradual decline in both production and manpower.

Ashington was served by a two-and-a-half-mile, double-track branch line to Linton, where it joined the British Rail system. Here there were extensive sidings with many locomotive sheds and workshops.

By 1970 the coal was transported via Ellington on a two-and- three-quarter-mile branch line. In the last year of production all Ashington's coal was transported by road.

At the peak of its productive life in 1930, Ashington Colliery employed 5,000 men, and its output was 1.5 million tons of coal a year from all its shafts and drifts.

The colliery was finally closed on the first of October 1986. For well over a hundred years, its miners had been proud that they were employed at what was known as 'The Premier Pit of the Northumberland Coalfield'.

Duke shaft in 1947

Ashington Colliery two months after closure

Seams worked at Ashington Colliery

1. High Main M.B. (Black Close)[1].
2. High Main (Diamond or Top Main).
3. Main Coal (Grey Coal).
4. Yard.
5. Maudlin (Bensham or 6/4).
6. Low Main (Five Quarter).
7. Brass Thill (Low Main).
8. Hutton (Plessey)[2].
9. Harvey (Beaumont).
10. Tilly.

11, 12. Busty (Top and Bottom Busty[3]).

13. 3/4.
14. Brockwell (Bandy).
15. Victoria.

Notes

1 The M.B. stands for Marine Band, which means that the seams were formed much later than the others.

2 It is possible that the Plessey was worked both top and bottom at Ashington, with the bottom Plessey called the Ruler or Bothal.

3 It is possible that the Bottom Busty was worked from the New Moor Shaft or the Connygarth Drift.

Backworth Collieries

'A', Maude and Eccles Pits

The village of Backworth lies six miles to the north east of Newcastle. A visitor to this quiet little village would find it hard to believe that it was once a hive of industry, once having 12 mines working within a three-mile radius.

The story of this group of collieries begins in 1818, when Backworth Collieries

'A' Pit and Maude shafts in 1905 Photograph Alan Oliver, Holystone

Eccles shaft, 1966

Limited sunk the A pit to a depth of 546ft. In 1820 the B pit followed, 500 yards to the north. As the century progressed the C, D, and E pits were sunk nearby, until on 9th June 1872 the company sunk the Maude pit.

So close was the Maude pit to the A pit that they occupy the same map reference: 88NZ301725. By this time the A pit was being used as a pumping and ventilation shaft — the ventilation being driven by means of a furnace at the shaft bottom.

On Friday 14th October 1881 the Maude pit's roof blew off in a severe storm; from that day until the day the pit closed, the miners always referred to a Friday as 'Windy Friday'. By the late 1890s the B, C, D and E pits had all closed down; the B pit heapstead having burnt down in 1866. This left the Maude as the main production unit in the group.

In 1896, 17 years before production in the British coal industry reached its peak, the Backworth Collieries, which were seeking to expand their business, bought out the Shiremoor Coal Company, the owner of the Algernon and Blue Bell pits. The latter was to close in 1915 owing to a shortage of manpower created by the First World War. It never reopened, though it stood for many years as a pumping station.

In the early 1900s the Backworth Group again expanded, this time by sinking a new shaft 200 yards from the Maude pit, but on the other side of the Whin Dyke fault. The sinking of this new shaft, named the Eccles pit after a company director Richard Eccles, commenced on 18th July 1905 and reached the Marshall Green seam at a depth of 1,440ft, making it the deepest in the coalfield.

Although the pit had reached the Marshall Green seam, this seam was never worked and the drawing level became the Busty seam inset.

The sinking of the Eccles pit was not without incident. During the operation one of the guide ropes slipped and fell to the bottom of the shaft. It was so long that it had to be painstakingly cut up piece by piece and removed.

By the time Eccles pit was sunk in 1905, horizontal steam winders were the norm, but the Backworth Company opted for the older and less efficient vertical type. This suggests that the Company had economised by using a redundant engine from one of the closed shafts.

Although the Maude and the Eccles shafts were only 200 yards apart, they were always classed as two separate collieries. Possibly this was due to the different markets that the two pits served. The Whin Dyke fault seemed to effect the quality of the coal, particularly its sulphur content. This view is supported by the fact that the washer was split into two halves, which separated the product of the two pits.

A Pit and Maude shafts in 1970. A Pit is in the foreground.

In 1927, the Company started to mechanise both mines underground, introducing rope-haulage and coal-cutting machines. This process was tragically interrupted in 1928 when a terrible explosion killed four men and injured eight.

By 1930 face conveyors had been introduced.

In 1931 a further expansion of the Company led to its amalgamation with the East Hollywell Coal Company, adding Fenwick Colliery and Church Colliery to the Group. It was at this time that the first pit baths were built, serving both pits.

Disaster struck again, in 1933, when an explosion killed three men.

The early 1930s saw a dramatic change in the Backworth landscape with the building of a washery to process the mines' coal. Its two giant coal hoppers dominated the surrounding countryside. This new washer replaced the Dolly washer, which was on the site of the old B pit and finally closed in 1940, although it stood until the early 1980s.

An unusual feature of the pit was its barium plant built in 1935. The barium-laden waters of the mine had plagued the life of the Colliery's pump men: barium was constantly clogging the pipes and blocking up the pumps. The plant turned what had been a nuisance into a a source of profit.

In 1943 the Maude pit was idle for nine days after the two cages collided in the shaft, wrecking its structures.

The winder on the Maude shaft changed in 1946 from steam power to electrical power. This was achieved by building the new winder house behind the old one, then removing the roof of the old winder house, before threading the ropes through (see illustration).

Eccles shaft was converted in a similar manner in 1948, but the old winder house was demolished.

After nationalisation the two pits were amalgamated into one unit and the writing was on the wall for the Maude pit. It closed on 2nd December 1960, leaving Eccles as the main production unit.

Nationalisation brought further changes, which completed the mechanisation of the pit and introduced 'skip winding' to the Eccles shaft, by fixing a three-ton skip under the cage.

The washery was used by other collieries to process their coal, until in 1970 a floor collapsed, killing one man. An investigation showed that the washery was suffering from metal fatigue, and it was closed down and demolished. Eccles coal was then sent to Weetslade to be washed, and later, for the last two years before the Colliery closed, to Bates Colliery.

During their lifetime the Maude and Eccles pits worked some 12 seams (see box below).

At its peak the Maude pit produced over 229,000 tons a year and employed 765 men. The Eccles pit produced over 225,000 tons a year and employed 708 men, making a total of 454,000 tons and 1,450 men between the two collieries.

The Maude and Eccles Collieries were served by what were known as the Backworth Locos. At first these locomotives took the coal from the washery to the

Steam locos in use at Backworth in 1972 Photographs Alan Oliver, Holystone

A Pit, Maude and Eccles shafts in 1982, after closure

Percy staithes, where the coal was loaded on to the coastal colliers. After the closure of the washery the coal was taken first to Weetslade and later to Blyth.

In 1978 the barium plant was closed; then, on 16th June 1980, production at Eccles Colliery ceased and with it the production of coal in the Backworth area. Over 168 years of mining had come to a close.

Seams worked at Backworth Collieries

1. **High Main.**
2. **Main Coal (Metal Coal at the Maude).**
3. **Yard.**
4. **Maudlin (Bensham).**
5. **Low Main (Five Quarter — only the Maude worked this seam).**
6. **Brass Thill (Low Main).**
7. **Harvey (Beaumont).**
8. **Tilly (Eccles only).**
9. **and 10. Top and Bottom Busty (the Maude only worked one of these seams and was known as the Busty).**
11. **Three Quarter.**
12. **Brockwell.**

Bardon Mill Colliery

Bardon Mill Colliery was situated alongside the Military Road next to the South Tyne river and the Newcastle to Carlisle railway, at map reference 87NY774646.

The Colliery was in fact a drift mine sunk in 1940 by J. Peperell, a local man who remained the owner till nationalisation. The drift was 340 yards long with a

Bardon Mill Colliery in 1973 Photograph Dennis Partis, Haltwhistle

Surface workers at Bardon Mill Colliery in 1960

one-in-three gradient, reaching the Little Limestone seam in the Upper Limestone Measures. This was the only seam ever worked.

The Colliery was never large, being composed of a series of smaller drifts that had been worked in the 1930s. Under the NCB's management the manpower employed at the Colliery rose from 100 men to a peak of 320 in the 1960s, then declining steadily until its closure in 1973.

The increased manpower under the NCB allowed the working of the two-foot-high seams by the long-wall method. These 120-yard, hand-filling faces were very hazardous and difficult to work owing to the existence of water-bearing strata above the coal.

The last manager of the mine, Mr Dennis Partis, described this seam as being "just like a big sponge, every time you broke into the roof, more water came in".

To cope with its water problems, the mine needed 39 pumps with each pumping 60 to 80 gallons per minute and six pumps delivering 600 gallons per minute. In all the mine was pumping 2 million gallons per day.

At its peak the mine's coal output was 139,000 tons per year, a marvellous testimony to the men's tenacity and determination to make the mine pay. Production was mainly for the power station market, with approximately 20 per cent for domestic use.

The mine was served by a railway link to the Newcastle to Carlisle main line and right up to its closure used steam locomotives.

Owing to faulted ground and worsening water problems the NCB decided to stop production and close the mine on 5th November 1973. After 33 years of struggle the water had finally won.

The closure of the last mine to be worked in the west of the coalfield came as a bitter blow to the local community as the pit was its chief source of employment.

Bedlington A Colliery in 1910 Photograph George Nairn, Chester le Street

Bedlington A Colliery

Bedlington A Pit was sunk in the village of Sleekburn, now better known as Bedlington station. (Map reference 81NZ274829.)

The Pit was originally known as Sleekburn A or as 'The Auld Pit', and sinking began in 1838 under the direction of the Bedlington Coal Company.

The first two shafts sunk were only 7ft. in diameter and 8ft. apart. They reached the 5ft.-6in.-thick Low Main seam at a depth of 600ft., and they shared with Seaton Deleval the distinction of being the only shafts in Northumberland having tandem headgear.

In 1875 it was decided to sink a shaft of 13ft. diameter, as the size of the old shafts was restricting the working of the mine. This shaft was to be sunk to the Yard seam at a depth of 400ft. and was then named the 'A' Pit, the old shafts becoming known as the 'B' Pits or the 'Little Pits'.

In 1888 the B Pits were laid in and production was concentrated at the A Pit.

In 1910 the B Pit was reopened and deepened to 957ft. to reach the Three Quarter seam and a new steam winder of the Robey Compact design was installed. This winder and the chimney of its boiler house were to remain until the day the Colliery closed.

In 1912 the A Pit was deepened to 774ft. to reach the Harvey seam.

Bedlington A Colliery washer in 1958
Photograph John Hughes

The A Pit was originally fitted with a Joycey steam engine, which was replaced in 1934 with an electric winder from the then-closed Barrington Colliery.

In 1934 a ventilation shaft was sunk. Until this time the ventilation of the mine was facilitated by the D Pit.

The 1930s economic depression created the conditions where the stronger coal companies were able to devour their weaker rivals. The Bedlington Coal Company was one of the former and, in 1934, took over first the Wallsend and Hebburn Coal Company and then the Netherton Coal Company.

These acquisitions were, however, 'small beer' compared with the £825,000 that the Company raised, by a public flotation, to take over the assets of the Hartley Mains Coal Company in 1943.

Although all the old companies retained their names, the parent company became known as the Bedlington Mains Coal Company — a name that, despite the size of the Company, had no time to become well known as nationalisation was only four years away.

During the 1950s under the NCB, Bedlington A Pit was modernised with a complete restructuring of the surface plant; a new washer was built; and underground shearer faces were introduced.

At its peak the Colliery produced 320,000 tons of coal a year and employed 980 men. It produced for a variety of markets, including household, steam, manufacturing and power stations.

Bedlington A was served by sidings on the west side of the Bedlington railway station on the British Rail Bedlington to Morpeth line.

By the end of the 1960s many of Bedlington's seams were exhausted, and all work had ceased in the Yard, Five Quarter and Harvey seams. By the beginning of the 1970s the Middle Main and Denton Low Main seams were all but worked out.

On 25th September 1971 the NCB announced that production was to end at the Bedlington A Pit. The last seam to be worked was the Busty and the last of the Busty's coals were drawn up the old B Pit shaft 133 years after it had been sunk.

In the course of the pit's development such illustrious names as Michael Longridge and George Stephenson had been associated with the name of Bedlington A.

Michael Longridge owned Bedlington Iron Works and, at one point, was a partner of George Stephenson, the inventor of the locomotive.

When the Pit finally closed the men either left the industry or transferred to the few local mines that remained open.

Bedlington A Colliery in 1954 showing tandom headgear
Photograph John Hughes, Chester le Street

Shaker picking belts of the type used at Bedlington A and B Pits. The shaker belts at Bedlington A Colliery were used as a location for the film 'Women in Love'.

Seams worked at Bedlington A Colliery

1. Moorland.
2. High Main (Top Main).
3. Main Coal.
4. Yard.
5. Maudlin (Bensham).
6. Low Main (Five Quarter).
7. Brass Thill (Low Main).
8. Hutton L. (Plessey).
9. Harvey (Beaumont).
10. Tilly (Denton Low Main).
11. Top Busty (Busty).
12. 3/4.

The A Pit drove a drift into the workings of the Bedlington E Pit and worked areas of the Yard, Bensham and Plessey seams. This area of workings was known as 'Watty's Drift'. When Bedlington F Pit closed, the A Pit workings were extended into the F Pit's take in the High Main.

Bedlington F Colliery

Bedlington F Colliery was originally known as the Bomarsund Pit and was sunk by the Barrington Coal Company. The village that grew with the pit itself became known as Bomarsund. The first shaft, the Hannah, named after the wife of one of the directors, as was then the tradition, was sunk at map reference 81NZ269847; the first sod being cut on 22nd August 1854.

This shaft was sunk to the High Main seam at a depth of 274ft., but before the seam could be properly won out the mine was found to be inundated with water and was subsequently abandoned.

Bedlington F Colliery in 1930

Shearer working in Main Coal seam 4th South

In 1904 the Bedlington Coal Company, which had taken over from the former owners, began pumping out the water from the disused shaft and re-entered the mine. On 18th July 1905 work began, deepening the shaft and reaching the Plessey seam on 6th January 1906, at a depth of 671ft.

The next project the Company undertook was the sinking of the Francis upcast shaft, which commenced on 17th June 1907 and reached the Lower Busty seam at a depth of 882ft. on 28th April 1908. This seam, however, was never worked.

At first the Colliery's coal was drawn from the shafts of the nearby Barrington mine, but by 1909 the colliery was completely independent.

The Bedlington F royalty was not a large one and by 1930 the mine was seeking to extend its area of exploitation. The Barrington Pit had closed in 1927 and it was decided to re-enter the workings of this colliery. This was achieved by driving a drift from the Plessey seam into the old Barrington take. This was completed by 1937 and provided a new lease of life for the Pit.

By the time the Pit was nationalised, in 1947, it was in a poor condition. However in this year new headgear was erected over the upcast shaft, making it able to draw coal. The headgear was not new but was salvaged from the Kitty shaft at Seghill.

The coal-drawing shaft was still using a steam winder and this was not to change until 1953, when this shaft inherited another Seghill cast-off, an electric winder.

In its lifetime the colliery worked a total of 10 seams with a mixed degree of success. At its peak it produced 231,000 tons of coal and employed 933 men. It always maintained a high degree of mechanisation, and was one of the first collieries to introduce shearer and plough faces.

Always restricted by the size of its boundaries, by 1960 it was also experiencing difficult geological problems. In 1965, on 22nd October, the NCB closed the Colliery. The fans remained powered to aid the ventilation of the nearby A Pit until 1968.

Miner using a bull-head electric drill in a High seam at Bedlington F Colliery
Photograph from Ross Miles, Ashington

Bedlington F Colliery in the 1920s Photograph from John Reed, Bedlington

Seams worked at Bomarsund

1. High Main.
2. Main Coal.
3. Yard.
4. Top Yard (Blake)[1].
5. Maudlin (Bensham).
6. Low Main (5/4)[2].
7. Brass Thill (Low Main)[3].
8. Hutton (Plessey).
9. Harvey (Beaumont)
10. Victoria (was known as the Barrington Victoria Bensham).

Notes

1 This seam was abandoned after one year.
2 This seam hit a washout within weeks.
3 In the Barrington area this seam was known as the Barrington Low Main.

Blackhill Colliery

Blackhill Colliery was sunk in the very north of Northumberland, being situated over two miles south west of the village of Scremerston (map reference 75NU863482) and close to the border town of Berwick-upon-Tweed.

In fact, Blackhill was an extension of the Scremerston mine and was sunk in 1942 to reach the Blackhill seam, which gave the mine its name. The mine's shaft was only 240ft. deep, but it was the proud boast of those who worked the Blackhill seam that they were one of the few groups of miners that not only worked the coal but had sunk the shafts of their colliery.

Once coal-drawing operations were underway at the new shaft, the older colliery at Scremerston was abandoned.

Blackhill Colliery 1959 Photograph Jack Parsons

Scremerston Colliery 1920 Photograph George Nairn, Chester-le-Street

Blackhill then became the most northerly colliery in England.

The seams in this area are the Scremerston Measures, but by the time the Blackhill Pit was sunk the Blackhill seam was the only seam left workable, the others having all been worked out.

In the short period between the sinking of the shaft and the onset of nationalisation the Colliery had two owners, John Watson and Co., a Scottish company which had undertaken the sinking of the pit, and Young Ltd., which was operating the mine prior to Vesting Day.

The mine ran with the minimum of mechanisation, winning the coal from short faces of 30 and 60 yards of low quality coal 2ft., 3in. thick. It is said that the practice of filling on to the bottom belt started at this colliery.

Working conditions were very difficult, with the miners having to deal with a severe water problem and numerous faults. Despite these problems the colliery produced 68,000 tons of coal a year with just 210 men.

Production was taken by road to satisfy the demands of the local market.

Foreman's Row Scremerston with Pit in background Photograph Beamish Museum

Blackhill Colliery 1959

Allerdean Drift 1963 Photograph Jack Parsons

In 1959 the NCB decided that the mine was far too uneconomic and announced its closure. Such was the importance of the mine to this isolated community that a vigorous local campaign was waged against the closure.

We are fortunate to have this campaign documented in a remarkable film, which vividly portrays the bitterness the men felt at the closure of their mine. The campaign, however, was to no avail and on 20th February 1959 the mine closed. Many men left the area to work in the pits further south.

There was a sad sequel to the closure. In 1960 some of the redundant miners joined forces with the Elsdon Coal Company and reopened the abandoned Allerdean Drift close to Colliery's site.

The first setback to this enterprise was the unexpected death of Mr Tommy Philips, the man who had been the driving force behind the reopening of the Drift. The loss of this capable man must have been a great blow to the morale of the men. However what was to follow was even more devastating.

In 1965 the main gate of the only face collapsed, killing one man and losing the face. This double tragedy brought 400 years of coal mining in Scemersdale to a close.

Burradon Colliery

Burradon Colliery was was sunk in 1820, by Lord Ravensworth and Partners, in the small Northumberland village of Burradon, three miles north of Newcastle. The Colliery's two shafts were sunk to a depth of 912ft. to the Low Main seam. (Map reference 88NZ274728.)

This pit was destined to have many owners in the course of its long life.

In 1849 the pit was sold to Carr and Co., the owners of the Wallsend Iron Works.

In 1856 Carr and Co. was declared bankrupt and the Colliery was sold, in September of that year, to Joseph Straker of Tynemouth for the sum of £29,800.

In 1860 a terrible explosion occurred at the mine, killing 76 men and boys. The mine was consequently sold to a Joshuah Bower of Leeds.

In 1879 the mine once again changed hands, this time to Nathaniel Green, Lambert and Partners, later to become the Burradon and Coxlodge Coal Company. This was the beginning of a more stable era at the Colliery that lasted until 1926, when, after a fire at the pit, a new heapstead and screens were built. By 1929 the coal company had changed hands because of bankruptcy and became known as the Hazelrigg and Burradon Coal Company,

Burradon Colliery 1950 Photograph Cris Smith, Brunswick

Face Conveyor feeding onto Main Gate Belt

which retained ownership of the mine until nationalisation.

The mine was never fully mechanised, although it did employ coal-cutting machines. When the mine finally closed it was a hand filling pit.

Although the mine had worked seven seams in the course of its lifetime, by the time it closed it was only working the main Coal seam in an area that had been left by Seghill mine.

At its peak the mine had produced over 215,000 tons of coal per year and employed 680 men.

The Colliery had once been connected to the Killingworth and Seaton Burn wagon way part of the old network of wagon ways used to transport the coal of the Northumberland mines in the 19th century. When it closed it was connected to the Wheetslade washer by a mile-long branch line.

By 1975 the reserves of the Colliery had dwindled to such an extent that the Colliery was no longer considered viable and was closed on 22nd November of that year.

Seams worked at Burradon Colliery

1. **High Main**
2. **Main Coal**
3. **Yard.**
4. **Maudlin (Bensham).**
5. **Low Main (Hartly Coal).**
6. **Brass Thill (Low Main).**
7. **Harvey (Beaumont).**

Choppington A Colliery in 1956 Photograph John Hughes, Chester le Street

Choppington A Colliery

Choppington A Colliery was only the second colliery to be sunk by the Bebside Coal Company. Sinking began, in 1857, in the village of Choppington, three miles south east of Morpeth (map reference 81NZ250841).

The first sinking was to the Low Main seam at 376ft. and later the shaft was

Close up of the coal shaft, 1954

deepened to the Beaumont seam at 589ft.

After the sinking of the Choppington B pit, the Company was in difficulties, and on 9th April 1925 went into voluntary liquidation. Five months later a new company was formed and both A and B Pits were opened up immediately.

The new company set about the modernisation of the A pit, erecting new steel headgears and building modern screens. This was to make the A pit the main pit in the group.

At first the colliery was worked using the board-and-pillar method of partial extraction, but later this was changed to long-wall mining and total extraction; with the long-wall method endless haulage was also introduced.

This was not the last modernisation programme the Colliery was to undertake. After nationalisation, in the 1950s, a new electric winders were installed in the coal and the upcast shafts and new screens were built. Underground, 200-yard mechanised shearer faces were installed with armoured face conveyors.

Working 12 seams during its lifetime, the Colliery's peak was an output of over 214,000 tons of coal a year and just over 630 men employed.

The Colliery was served by a 1.2-mile branch line to the main Morpeth British Rail line, crossing the Willow burn on a wooden viaduct.

Choppington A was another colliery to fall prey to the rationalisation of the 1960s. The pit closed on 16th July 1966, abandoning its reserves in the Brockwell and the Victoria seams.

Seams worked at Choppington A Colliery

1. Yard.
2. Maudlin (Bensham).
3. Low Main (Five Quarter).
4. Brass Thill (Low Main).
5. Hutton (Plessey).
6. Harvey (Beaumont).
7. Tilly (Denton Low Main).
8. Top Busty.
9. Bottom Busty
10. Three Quarter.
11. Brockwell (Bandy).

In the Choppington area the Brockwell seam is known as the Bandy, the Victoria as the Brockwell, and the Marshal Green as the Victoria. This is an indication of how complicated the classification of seams at any one colliery can be.

The 12th seam worked at Choppington was the "One Foot Ten Inches". This may have been the NCB's Hodge seam.

Coal shaft banksman, 1954

Choppington A miners' banner 1956 Photograph Mrs Ord, Bedlington

Crofton Mill Colliery in 1969

Crofton Mill Colliery

Crofton Mill Colliery was so called because it was sunk on the site of an old mill, close to the centre of Blyth (map reference 81NZ317810).

Sinking began on 26th January 1885 by the Cowpen and North Seaton Coal Company, which sank the shaft to the Low Main seam at a depth of 558ft. and made an inset to the Yard seam. The first 80 feet of the shaft was lined with sheets of steel riveted and corked like the hull of a ship. This procedure, known as tubbing,

Colliery officials on the day of closure in 1969

was necessary as the site of the sinking was below the level of the spring high tides. Because of its nearness to Blyth town centre, the headgears were very low although the pulley wheels were 14 feet in diameter.

Crofton had only one shaft. Its second means of escape was by way of what was then called the North Pit, which after 1932 became the Bates Pit. Crofton Mill was also connected underground to the Isabella Colliery.

For ventilation it shared a shaft of the old Hannah Foster Pit, one-and-a-quarter miles away at South Newsham. Although Crofton had only one shaft to the surface, it had an underground shaft, or staple shaft, linking the Low Main seam to the Denton Low Main seam. The staple and the shaft were only 50 yards apart and coal was drawn from the Denton Low Main seam up the staple and then up the main shaft. The staple shaft had closed by the 1920s.

The owner of the Crofton mine formed a public company, the Cowpen Coal Company, in 1884 and, although it retained its name until nationalisation, this company was taken over in 1928 by the Mickly Coal Company.

Crofton worked ten seams (see box below), although in tracing this from a study of the records some difficulty arises as the Cowpen Company worked all its pits as more or less one unit.

The Plessey seam was worked out to sea, and as the Top and Bottom Plessey seams came within 6 inches of each other they were worked, taking both seams together

Underground loco sheds in 1966

in an area known as the narrow boards. I have found no record of this happening elsewhere in the coalfield in the Plessey seam.

Crofton Mill Colliery employed many different methods of mining its seams and was mechanised to a high degree, working its narrow boards with Anderson Boyd arc wall shearers and shuttle cars.

Peak annual coal output reached 366,000 tons and a maximum 952 men were employed. In its last years nearly all production went to power stations. The mine was linked to the British Rail branch line from Newsham to the South Blyth staithes. Production stopped at Crofton on 18th July 1969 and the men were transferred to local pits.

Coal shaft showing creeper to screens in 1969

Anderson Boyd arc wall shearer of the type used in narrow boards at Crofton Mill Pit

Seams worked at Crofton Mill

1. **High Main.**
2. **Main Coal.**
3. **Yard.**
4. **Maudlin (Bensham).**
5. **Low Main (Five Quarter).**
6. **Brass Thill (Low Main, the main drawing inset).**
7. **Hutton (Plessey).** } **narrow boards**
8. **Plessey (Bottom Plessey).** } **narrow boards**
9. **Harvey (Beaumont).**
10. **Tilly (Denton Low Main).**

Dinnington and Williams Collieries

Dinnington and Williams collieries are again an example of two separate units whose development is so interconnected that they have to be described alongside each other.

The sinking of Dinnington colliery was undertaken by John Bowes & Partners in 1867 in the village of Brunswick (at map reference 88NZ231727) and not in the village of Dinnington, as may be supposed

Dinnington Colliery 1900

Dinnington Colliery 1915. Left to right: Hester upcast, Augusta and Beaumont (West)

from the colliery's name. John Bowes & Partners were part of a much bigger County Durham concern known as The Grand Allies.

The first shaft sunk was called the 'Augusta' shaft after Mrs Augusta Palmer, who cut the first sod and was the wife of one of the partners. This shaft was sunk to the High Main seam at 180ft.

The Augusta shaft was followed by a second shaft in 1873 and was sunk to the Low Main seam at a depth of 600ft. This shaft may have been called the Engine or East shaft.

Both the High Main seam and the Low Main seam were four feet thick. By the time the Low Main seam came on stream the pit was producing 800 tons a day from its two shafts.

By 1899 John Bowes & Partners had decided to concentrate their efforts in County Durham and sold off their pits in Northumberland.

On 24th June 1899 Dinnington and Seaton Burn Collieries were sold to the Seaton Burn Coal Company Ltd. for £70.000.

In 1901 the new owners implemented a modernisation programme at Dinnington, installing a new winder in the Augusta shaft. This winder was a Steam Horizontal

Dinnington Colliery 1920 Photograph Chris Smith, Brunswick Village

Winder built by Andrew Barclay and Sons of Kilmarnock and was believed at that time to be the biggest in the area.

New screens were built and the company began sinking a new shaft to the Beaumont seam at a depth of 862ft.; this shaft became known as the Beaumont or West shaft.

This phase of the modernisation of the Colliery was complete by the end of 1902.

In 1904 a fourth shaft was sunk for ventilation purposes. This shaft was also sunk to the Beaumont seam to a depth of 798 ft. and was called the Hester shaft. It was equipped with a massive waddle fan. By this time the Engine or East shaft was used for pumping purposes only.

In 1908 a brickworks was built at the Pit and a Belgian kiln was installed with 26 chambers, each chamber holding 6,500 bricks.

The workings of the Colliery were restricted by a fault that runs to the north of Dinnington. Rather than drive through the fault the company decided that it would be cheaper to sink a new shaft one-and- a-quarter miles north west of Dinnington at Mill Hill Farm.

This new shaft was to become Williams Colliery and was sunk to the Low Main seam at 588ft.

In 1938 the Seaton Burn Coal Company was liquidated and the mine again changed hands when it was acquired by Hartly Main Collieries Ltd.

Under the new company, Dinnington Colliery was further modernised when in 1940 the mine was electrified, including the installation of new electric winders in the coal shafts. The mine's chimneys were demolished and the Engine shaft was laid in. At some point the waddle fan was replaced by a modern fan.

In 1943, four years before nationalisation, the Bedlington Mains Coal Company took over the management of the mine.

Even after nationalisation Williams Colliery was not mechanised, winning the coal by the board-and-pillar method of partial extraction and short handfilling faces 80, 100 and 120 yards long.

In 1954 the NCB decided to concentrate on two new drift mines,Havannah and Brenkley that they had sunk in the area and on July 16 th of that year production ceased at the Williams pit and the men were dispersed to local collieries.

Williams Pit produced 80,000 tons of coal a year from three seams and employed 230 men. Dinnington worked eight seams in its lifetime and produced over

Dinnington Colliery 1920 Photograph Chris Smith

Dinnington Colliery pit chimney . . .

Going . . .

. . . Gone in 1940 to make way for electric winders

Photographs Chris Smith

Williams Pit 1964, ten years after closure Photograph Mr Hall, Dinnington

142,000 tons of coal at its peak and employed 472 men.

The product from the Williams Pit was mainly for the household market and power stations, while Dinnington produced a high-quality gas coal from the Beaumont seam — the product of its other seams was sold to the manufacturing and household markets.

After the closure of Williams Pit Dinnington continued, but by 1960 the NCB decided that the shafts were too far away from the workable reserves and that the ground between them was too faulted.

On the 26th February of that year the mine was closed and the reserves in the Beaumont seam were worked from Brenkley. All that remained at Dinnington was the brickworks and this in turn closed one year later.

Seams worked at Dinnington and Williams Collieries

Dinnington

1. **High Main.**
2. **Main Coal.**
3. **Yard.**
4. **Brass Thill (Low Main).**
5. **Plessey.**
6. **Harvey (Beaumont).**
7. **Top Busty (Upper Busty).**
8. **Bottom Busty (Lower Busty).**

Williams

1. **Main Coal.**
2. **Yard.**
3. **Brass Thill (Low Main).**

East Walbottle and Prestwick Collieries

Although East Walbottle and Prestwick Collieries had separate origins, their development became so interlinked that at a certain point they have to be considered as one unit.

Prestwick Colliery was situated three-quarters of a mile south of the village of Prestwick, close to Newcastle Airport (map ref. 88NZ184714).

There is evidence of several shafts

East Walbottle Colliery in 1956: surface workers and apprentices in for ground
Photograph Miles Watson, Dinnington

Aerial ropeway at Walbottle Colliery in 1911 Photograph Margaret Stalker

Prestwick screens in the 1930s Photograph Margaret Stalker

having been sunk in the area in the 18th century. One of these, the Phylis Pit, survived until 1880. A landsale pit, it was sunk to the Brockwell seam at a depth of 228 feet, and was owned by the Prestwick Coal Company.

In 1904 the Company sank two more shafts alongside the Newcastle-Ponteland railway, again to a depth of 210ft. and to the Brockwell seam. One of these was christened the Lizzy Anne, no doubt after the daughter or wife of a Company directors, as was the fashion.

In an effort to open up a wider market for its product, screens and sidings were built alongside the new sinkings. The mine worked successfully until 1924, by which time the royalty had become exhausted and the mine was laid idle.

The East Walbottle Coal Company had engaged in a similar venture when in 1908 it sank two shafts at its East Walbottle Colliery, on the west side of the village of Dinnington one mile north of Newcastle Airport.

These shafts were sunk to a depth of 180 feet to the Beaumont seam and were known as the Robert Pit. This was a small landsale pit producing between 80 and 100 tons of coal a day. In 1911 the company made an arrangement with the Prestwick Coal Company to use the screens at the latter's Prestwick Colliery.

In order to transport the coal to the screens, they built an aerial flight between the two collieries, a distance of one-and-three-quarter miles. This kept the screens at Prestwick employed while that colliery lay idle in 1924.

Timbering up single jib cutter in Beaumont seam, 1940. Left to right: Joe Ermuyten, Joss Bates and Sam Leader Photograph Miles Watson

In 1925 the Prestwick Coal Company acquired a new area of coal to exploit, the Graham royalty, which they acquired from the North Walbottle Coal Company in exchange for the Bell royalty. This allowed them to reopen Prestwick Colliery the same year, having formed a new company, the Callerton Coal Company.

So closely were the East Walbottle Coal Company and this new company working together that a merger was inevitable, and it took place in 1938. The directors of the two companies remained virtually the same and the name of the East Walbottle Coal Company was kept until nationalisation.

A miner with a minor, East Walbottle 1966 Photograph Miles Watson

The merger brought new investment to the collieries and they were both electrified underground.

The collieries worked a short-wall and a long-wall system, the lengths of the faces being 60 yards and 120 yards respectively.

The 60-yard faces were worked in the shallower measures where the roof conditions were difficult.

Coal cutters and conveyor belts were employed on the faces and endless rope haulage was used to transport the tubs to the shaft, with pit ponies taking supplies in-bye.

After nationalisation both manpower and production at the collieries increased. In an effort to produce 'round' coal — large lumps of coal suitable for the household market — the NCB introduced trepanners to cut the coal in the West Brockwell District and several experiments were made using ploughs.

Similar experiments in using ploughs to cut coal were at that time being made in other parts of the Northumberland coalfield. The method consists of hauling a large steel wedge along the coal face by a remote hauler placed in the main gate, the object being to pare the coal from the face. The difficulties arose when the coal was inconsistent in its degree of hardness. The plough would cut into the softer coal and bounce off the harder coal. Although this method was attractive in that the machinery was inexpensive, where the coal yielded in this uneven way it was dangerous.

Although there was further experimentation with the aim of achieving fully mechanised faces the collieries remained basically semi-mechanised, using coal cutters to undercut the faces, then drilling, firing and hand filling.

An administration centre was built by the NCB at Prestwick, where the men's wages were paid and the mine's materials were ordered.

In 1952, when the NCB stopped their pumping operation at the South Elswick pit, the north side of East Walbottle

Surface workers at East Walbottle in 1908. Clarrie Stalker is in the scull cap
Photograph Margaret Stalker

flooded despite the distance between the two collieries.

The position of the two collieries on the edge of the coalfield — where the seams decline in number and tilt towards the surface — was responsible for the relatively shallow depth of the shafts. Despite the small number of seams available to the collieries, they were able to produce between them over 180,000 ton of coal a year with 400 men. No separate production figures exist for the two collieries because of the NCB's practice of classing them as one unit.

By 1966 the mines' reserves were beginning to dwindle, and it was announced on 29th October 1966 that the Prestwick and East Walbottle Collieries were finally to close. In this area of the coalfield the NCB decided to concentrate production on the Havannah Drift.

The shafts of the Prestwick mine were retained for ventilation of the Havannah mine and the Prestwick West Brockwell District was worked from Havannah using the Prestwick transferees. A sad but familiar outcome.

Seams worked at East Walbottle and Prestwick Collieries

Prestwick Colliery

1. Main Coal.
2. Harvey (Beaumont or Engine).
3. Top Busty.
4. Bottom Busty.
5. Brockwell.

East Walbottle Colliery

1. Harvey (Beaumont or Engine).
2. Top Busty.
3. Bottom Busty.

Prestwick Collieries and screens in 1964

Hazlerigg Colliery

The village of Hazlerigg is situated two miles north of Newcastle and it was here, in 1892, that the Burradon and Coxlodge Coal Company began the sinking of the first shaft of the Colliery at map reference 88NZ228718.

The shaft was sunk to the Low Main seam at a depth of 780ft.; it was unusual in that it was 16ft. in diameter, the widest shaft in Northumberland at the time.

The shaft was in fact two shafts, being divided down its centre. One half was equipped with two small cages and drew from the High Main seam, while the other half had two large cages and drew from the Low Main seam. These two shafts were used for all the man riding at the Colliery.

A second shaft was sunk for ventilation purposes and was 10ft. in diameter and at first was a furnace shaft, later to be converted to fan-driven ventilation. This shaft like the first was sunk to the Low Main seam at 760ft.

In 1927 a small headgear was erected

Hazlerigg Colliery 1964 during salvage operations. Foreground Mr George W. Brooks, the last manager of the mine Photograph George W. Brooks

Remains of middle engine winder on Brunton to Shields wagon way once used by Hazlerigg Colliery

above the ventilation shaft and a small cage capable of riding 12 men was installed.

The mine was part of a complex of old workings to the north of Newcastle, covering an area of 16 square miles. Pumps had been established in an old shaft of the Brunton Colliery to pump out the Low Main seam of the Burn Pit district.

Pumping operations were also carried out from the Victoria shaft of the old Coxlodge mine, which had closed before the sinking of Hazlerigg Colliery. Despite the size of this pumping operation, water was always a problem.

The shafts of Hazlerigg Colliery were originally equipped with steam winders and were not replaced by electric winders until the 1950s, after nationalisation. In order not to disrupt production, a new winder house was built at the back of the Low Main's old steam winder and, when it was finished, the old winder houses were demolished. The High Main winder fell into disuse at this point.

In the course of its lifetime the pit had two owners, the second taking over in 1929. This new company, the Hazlerigg and Burradon Coal Company, was given financial backing by the Mickley Coal Company.

At its peak the mine produced over 208,000 tons of coal a year, working eight seams, and employed 740 men.

The mine was served by a railway line via Weetslade Colliery to the Holywell junction on the British Rail network.

Hazelrigg suffered the same fate as the other collieries in the area when the NCB opened the Havannah and Brenkely drift mines. All the Pit's reserves in the Plessey, Bottom Busty and Brockwell seams were lost to the new drifts and the Colliery closed on 2nd April 1964, with the men transferring to the new drifts.

Seams worked at Hazlerigg Colliery

1. **High Main.**
2. **Main Coal.**
3. **Maudlin (Bensham).**
4. **Yard.**
5. **Brass Till (Low Main).**
6. **Hutton (Plessey).**
7. **Harvey (Beaumont).**
8. **Top Busty.**

Longhirst Drift

This drift mine was sunk just outside the village of Longhirst near Ashington in 1956 by the NCB. Two drifts were driven, the first having a gradient of one in four was 1,000 yards long and the second was 1,200 yards, falling at a gradient of one in six.

The purpose of these new drifts was to reach an area of coal that had been cut off by a horseshoe-shaped fault. Three collieries had tried to reach this coal: Ashington New Moor shaft from the east; Stobswood from the north; and the Old Moor shaft from Linton, the only one to have any success and this in the Yard seam.

The mine was a modern set-up from its inception, winning the coal with shearers feeding on to armoured face conveyors, which in turn fed the product on to a belt system that took the coal all the way to the screens.

An attempt to use German ploughs on the face was rejected after a trial period.

Longhirst's claim to fame came in 1965, when it became the first colliery in Britain to achieve a production level of 1,000 tons of coal a shift off a single coal face; this

Longhirst 1958

Sinking Main drift (Coal drift)

Sinking Back drift (Fan drift)

was in the Diamond seam. The NCB, ever eager to exploit the propaganda advantage of such an achievement, made a film entitled 'The Longhirst Story'. There is no record of how long the film ran, but the colliery's ability to sustain the record once they had proved it possible was short lived.

By 1969 this mine was the only one left to the west of the Ashington system. The NCB had been already discussing the possibility that the manpower would be better employed at Ellington Colliery, when in the March of that year the shearer in the Plessey seam hit a washout.

The men made great efforts to move the shearer and the face equipment quickly to the Beaumont seam, which was under development, but within weeks the new face hit a massive fault. The men thought that this was just the excuse that the NCB was looking for to close the mine; this it did on 15th March 1969, transferring the workforce to Ellington.

Longhirst had exceeded its intended life expectancy of 10 years by 3 years. In this short life it had worked eight seams despite many difficulties presented by faulted ground that often caused the seams to disappear. It produced in excess of 400,000 tons a year and employed over 800 men.

Seams worked at Longhirst Drift

1. High Main (Diamond).
2. Main (Middle Main F1).
3. Yard G2 (Bentnink).
4. Low Main (5/4).
5. Brass Thill (Low Main).
6. Hutton (Plessey).
7. Harvey (Beaumont).
8. Top Busty Q2.

The Montague Collieries

The Montague story is that of two pits, the Montague Caroline and the Montague View Pits.

It begins in 1750 when Newcastle was expanding its coal production to fuel the furnaces of Britain's Industrial Revolution. In that year the Montague family sank the Caroline Pit in Slatyford Lane, Denton Burn, in the West End of Newcastle (map reference 88NZ203659). The shaft was

Montague Caroline Colliery in 1910 Photograph West Newcastle Local Studies

Endless rope haulage system of the type used in Kitty's Drift

sunk to the Brockwell seam at a depth of 572ft.

By 1765 they had completed the sinking of a second pit in the Scotswood area (map reference 88NZ197645). This sinking took the shafts to just below the Bottom Busty seam at 740ft.

These two pits became known as the High and Low Monty, the high being the Caroline and the low the View.

Shortly after the turn of the 19th century the Pits were laid idle, and in 1807 the Montague family sold them to Messrs. Cookson and Cuthbertson. This partnership operated the mines until 1857, when after another period of idleness the Pits were again sold, this time to the partnership of Benson and Hawthorn. In 1867 Hawthorn pulled out of the partnership, leaving Benson in sole charge. By the turn of the century Benson was joined by his son, who on his father's death took control of the mines.

On 25th March 1925 disaster struck the View Pit when an inrush of water trapped and killed 38 men and boys. It took the rescuers several weeks before the water was pumped out of the mine and the bodies recovered.

The mine was closed after the tragedy for three years. To reopen the mine Benson brought men from his Fourstones Drift mine to carry out the necessary work. After reopening, the Pit mainly mined seggar clay for Benson's brickworks.

In 1931 the Mickly Coal Company took over the mines from Benson and in 1934 they closed the View Pit down, concentrating their efforts on the Caroline Pit.

We can only speculate as to whether guilt or shame played any role in Benson's decision to part with the mine.

The Mickly Coal Company set about reorganising the Caroline Pit. At the time of the takeover the mine was basically a landsale mine but had utilised part of the famous 'Kitty's Drift', which in the early 1800s was used to transport the coal underground from Kenton Colliery to the

The Caroline Pit, 1925 Photograph Prof. Norman McCord, Newcastle University

staithes at Scotswood. As the entrance to this drift was close to the View Pit, the Mickly Coal Company used it to take the Caroline's coal to the screens at the now-closed View Pit.

Originally Kitty's Drift used a massive steam winder to haul the tubs the two-and-a-half miles to the View Pit screens, but this was replaced in 1933 by a 250-horsepower electric winder.

The Mickly Coal Company also drove a drift at a gradient of one in three from the Beaumont seam to intercept Kitty's Drift. This was named the Bates Drift, after a director of the Mickly Coal Company.

Another drift was driven, called the Fan pit level drift. This 980-yard drift allowed the tubs to be taken from the shaft up to the Kitty's Drift level and on to the View Pit.

This created a complex and extensive underground endless rope haulage system, in places up to six miles in length.

After nationalisation little changed at the Caroline Pit apart from a few experiments in mechanisation. By this time the Colliery was approaching its 200th year and it was by any standards an old pit, still

The View Pit in 1925, after the disaster
Photograph Evening Chronicle

sporting its wooden headgear, which was to remain until it closed.

Despite its age, the Pit at its peak produced a little under 220,000 tons of coal a year and employed around 900 men. In its lifetime the pit worked 11 seams.

By 1959 the fuel crisis of the post-war years had subsided, cheap oil was becoming the fashion of the day, and the NCB was looking to cut down production. It was decided that the reserves remaining could be worked from the near by North Wallbottle Colliery.

The Colliery closed on 13th November 1959 after 209 years of mining coal.

Seams worked at the Montague Collieries

1. Main coal (Stone Coal).
2. Yard.
3. Maudling (Five quarter).
4. Plessey (Low Main).
5. Harvey (Beaumont or Engine).
6. Hodge.
7. Tilley.[1]
8. Top Busty (Six Quarter).
9. Bottom Busty (Busty).
10. Three Quarter (Three Quarter Main).
11. Brockwell

Note

1 The Caroline Pit worked a district at this level called the seam pit level. Whether the Tilly split or another seam was worked at this level is not clear.

Nelson Colliery

On 16th May 1929 two coal companies, the Cramlington and the Seaton Deleval, came together to form Hartley Mains Collieries Limited. This new company, in its endeavours to exploit new reserves, sank four shafts in the Cramlington area in order to reach coal that had been cut off from the existing collieries by faulted ground.

Two of these new shafts, the Joy and the Nancy, failed almost immediately. The third was called the Gloria and will be dealt with in volume II. The fourth was the Nelson and was sunk in 1934 at map reference 88NZ260778, to the west of the town of Cramlington.

The coal shaft was sunk to 360ft. to reach the Plessey seam. The back shaft was sunk to the 5/4 seam and had a peculiar extension, which was neither a drift nor a shaft, to reach the Plessey seam. The gradient of this extension was so steep that it had to have steps cut into it and it was officially classed as a staple shaft.

Nelson Colliery 1935 Photograph Davy Reed, Nelson Village

Shot firer stemming coal face

The mine was so successful that a small village grew up around it. Nelson village still survives today, complete with its welfare hall, close to Cramlington's new town centre.

Nelson Colliery was what many miners would describe as a 'Blackin' Factory' — meaning it was small and backward. Till the day it closed the mine was worked almost exclusively by hand methods, the transport of coal and materials being by pit pony.

There is record that the manager of the mine, prior to nationalisation, was fined for not keeping the underground roadways up to the minimum specifications laid down by the Mines and Quarries Act. Anyone who is familiar with how infrequent such prosecutions were will know that these roadways must have been in a very bad condition to have invoked the wrath of Her Majesty's Inspectorate.

The coal from the mine was transported by an endless rope haulage system to the screens at Shankhouse, a distance of a little over a mile. The motive force for this system was provided by an engine that also drove the endless rope haulage system at Hartford Colliery. Nationalisation seemed to have passed this pit by as there was little subsequent change and, while efforts were made locally to improve production and manpower was increased, the rise in the number of employees coincided with a fall in production.

By 1957 the mine was placed on a one-shift system and on 4th January 1958 was closed, the men transferring to other local collieries.

This was a colliery whose peak production did not coincide with peak manpower figures. The maximum number of men it employed was 500 and its maximum tonnage in a year was over 180,000 tons.

Seams worked at Nelson Colliery

1. **Low Main (5/4).**
2. **Brass Thill (Low Main).**
3. **Hutton (Plessey).**

Newbiggin Colliery

Newbiggin Colliery was sunk on the Northumberland coast, three-and-a-half miles north of Blyth in the small town from which it derives its name. The coal company Newbiggin Collieries Limited began sinking the No. 1 and the No. 2 shafts on 9th March 1908 at map reference 81NZ309886, but within a short space of time serious difficulties were encountered.

The problems were created by running sand in the strata at a depth of 14ft. The sinkers pressed on for another 11ft., when they were forced to halt operations and take test borings, which revealed hard

Newbiggin Colliery, 1929 Photograph J. Tuck Senior

rock a further 74ft. below the sand.

As was the practice on many occasions in the North East, a German company was employed to overcome the sinking problems. On this occasion Haniel and Lugg of Dusseldorf was commissioned and work recommenced on 20th November 1908 using the drop-shaft method.

The drop-shaft method consists of forcing a steel, open-ended cylinder the diameter of the shaft into the sand with the aid of hydraulic rams. One cylinder is forced into the ground, then a second cylinder is bolted on to the first, and that in turn is forced down until a continuous steel tube is formed through the soft ground.

Unfortunately this was not an end of the troubles. In 1909 one of the sinkers, a Mr E. Bolton, was drowned in the shaft and a King's Medal for bravery was awarded to Mr A. Peebles for his brave attempts to save the drowning man.

Despite all the problems the Plessey seam was eventually reached at a depth of 870ft.

The coal company could not be accused of lack of confidence in the project as they had taken the unusual decision to build all the surface buildings before starting to sink the shafts, and had even started working on the screens.

Having made such a large financial commitment they found it almost impossible to back out once problems were encountered.

For its time Newbiggin was a relatively modern mine, employing endless haulers and battery-driven locomotives to transport the coal underground. On the coal faces and in the advanced headings ark wall shearers were used for cutting the coal.

Newbiggin was linked to the Ashington rail system via a half-mile branch to the Lynemouth and Woodhorn lines. There was also a three-quarter mile 'tub run' from the shaft to the screens.

In 1956 the NCB was developing the philosophy that the biggest was always the best and began the modernisation of Lynemouth Colliery, upgrading it to a million-ton colliery. The close proximity of Newbiggin to this development was to its detriment and it was closed on 10th November 1967 and the men transferred to Lynemouth.

At its peak Newbiggin Colliery had produced 268,000 tons of coal and employed 1,150 men.

Seams worked at Newbiggin Colliery

1. **High Main E.**
2. **High Main E2.**
3. **Main Coal.**
4. **Maudlin (Bensham).**
5. **Low Main (5/4).**
6. **Yard.**
7. **Brass Thill (Low Main).**
8. **Hutton (Plessey).**
9. **Plessey M (Bottom Plessey).**
10. **In the NCB Abandoned Seams Records there is an unnamed seam worked at this Colliery. This may have been the Beaumont seam.**

Seaton Deleval Colliery, 1910, showing all six shafts Photograph Alan Oliver, Holyston

Seaton Deleval Colliery

The sinking of the Seaton Deleval mine was started in 1838 by the Seaton Deleval Coal Company. Seaton Deleval lies more than two miles to the south of Blyth (map reference 88NZ299763).

A total of eight shafts was finally sunk. The A, B, C, D, E and F shafts were all coal-drawing shafts designed to take corves, a type of basket that was used at the time to carry the coal to the surface.

These shafts were sunk in pairs, in each case only 10 feet apart and 8 feet in diameter. The first two to be sunk, the A and B, were sunk to a depth of 255ft. to the High Main seam; and the C and D shafts to just below the Low Main seam at a depth of 638ft.

Although the E and F shafts were sunk to the same depth as the C and D shafts, they were used to draw coal not from the

Low Main seam but from the Yard seam by means of an inset at a depth of 447ft.

These six shafts, with their tandem headgear, must have created an impressive skyline for the surrounding area.

Tandem headgear was a sight only to be seen in Northumberland at this colliery and at Bedlington A.

The engine and pumping shafts, although of similar dimensions to the other shafts, were not sunk in such close proximity to each other and did not have the distinctive tandem headgear. These were sunk to 569ft. to the Low main seam.

All eight shafts had vertical steam engines of the lever type.

In 1848 further work was carried out on the A and B shafts, sinking them further to the Low Main Level at 630ft., and a furnace was constructed in the shaft bottom for ventilation. This furnace was later replaced by a boiler with a pressure of 33lbs per sq. in. Steam jets from the boiler were then blown up the shaft, creating a strong flow of air to facilitate the mine's ventilation. This method of ventilation was invented by T.E. Foster, the brother of George Baker Foster who led the rescue at the ill-fated Hartly Colliery.

Part of this formidable mine complex was a gas works that provided lighting not just for the Pit and the nearby New Hartly Colliery, but also for the miners' cottages.

The Colliery workshops, engine sheds and blacksmith's shops stand to this day and are part of the Seaton Delaval Industrial Estate.

In 1923 the engine and pumping shafts

Seaton Deleval Colliery from loco sheds, 1912 Photograph Derick Charlton, Newcastle

The old pumping and engine shafts being demolished in 1923
Photograph Tom Allen, Seaton Deleval

were laid in, the headgear pulled down, and the surrounding buildings demolished.

In 1929 the Seaton Deleval Coal Company merged with the Cramlington Coal Company to form Hartly Mains Collieries Ltd., a public company under whose direction Seaton Deleval Colliery would undergo a transformation.

Endless rope haulage, conveyor belts, and Anderson and Boyd coal cutters were installed underground and, in 1932, the company began the electrification of the colliery.

The A and B shafts were fitted with an electric fan and an electric winder. A single cage in the A shaft was to be used for carrying men while the C and D shafts became the main coal-drawing shafts. They were also fitted with an electric winder housed in the old winder house.

This was the end of the useful life of the E and F shafts, although their wooden headgear remained for a few years before they met the same fate as the pumping and engine shaft. They were finally demolished shortly before 1940.

In March 1943 the Hartly Mains Company became a part of the Bedlington Mains Company, but few or no changes were made by the new company to the Seaton Deleval Colliery. After nationalisation the NCB built a new heapstead and screens. Locomotives were introduced underground and the faces were mechanised to a degree.

Seaton Colliery was served by a four-mile rail link with the staithes at Percy Main and Hawdon. At its peak the mine produced over 231,000 tons of coal a year and employed 840 men.

In August 1956 Seaton Deleval Colliery was put on to single-shift working. This old colliery was nearing the end of its life and it was finally closed on 27th May 1960.

E and F shafts in 1925 Photograph Tom Allen

Seaton Deleval Colliery, 1933 Photograph Tom Allen

Seaton Deleval Colliery, 1956 Photograph Derick Charlton, Newcastle

Miners working in the Grey seam in 1908

Seams worked at Seaton Delaval Colliery

1. Moorland Coal.
2. High Main.
3. Main Coal (Grey).
4. Top Yard (Blake).
5. Yard.
6. Maudling (Bensham).
7. Low Main (Stone or Five Quarter)
8. Brass Thill (Low Main).
9. Hutton (Plessey).

According to the NCB's Abandon Seams Plans, Seaton Delaval also worked an unnamed seam around the 1840s. This may have been the Beaumont seam or a seam above the Moorland seam.

Seghill Colliery

Seghill is a small village more than four miles to the north of Newcastle. The name of the original owners who sunk the first shafts of the Seghill Colliery (map reference 88NZ289748) in 1824 appears to be lost. Records for the period between 1824 and 1856 refer to them as the owners of Seghill Colliery and later as the owners of Seghill and Burradon Collieries. Burradon, a nearby colliery, must have been a later acquisition of the owners.

There is evidence that the Colliery went bankrupt and was sold to a A.J. Carr and later, in 1878, to Laycock and Nicholson, a partnership that was to last until 1878.

The first shaft of the Colliery was the Engine shaft, which was sunk to a depth of 720 feet. A report of the time states that the shaft was taken 240ft. past the Low Main seam. As this is far too deep for a sump, it is probable that the shaft was originally sunk to the Beaumont seam, also known as the Engine seam. This would account for the name of the shaft.

A second shaft known as the John shaft was sunk to the Bensham seam at 318ft. A

Seghill Colliery 1873

Seghill Colliery 1962
Photograph Northumberland County Records Office

third shaft was sunk purely for the purposes of ventilation. This shaft was the same depth as the Engine shaft and housed the furnace.

There were still two shafts to be sunk. The 'Success' to a depth of 150ft. to the level of the High Main seam, and the 'Major', depth 228ft., to the Grey or Main seam. A record of the exact location of these shafts, like the name of the first owners, appears to be lost.

After 1890 Joseph Laycock took sole control of the mine and it was in his period of ownership that the famous song 'The dirty blackleg miner' was written; it named the Seghill mine as a place that harboured hidden dangers for any miner foolish enough to work while the men were on strike.

By 1920 the mine was suffering from a long-term lack of investment. To recapitalise the mine the new company Seghill Collieries was floated, with Sir Walton Brown, Sir Francis Blake and Joseph Laycock as the main directors. It was not, however, until 1929 that the modernisation plans came to fruition. The plan included the removal of all the wooden head gear of the shafts, the removal of the steam winding engines, and the sinking of a fifth shaft. The new shaft was called the 'Kitty' shaft and was sunk alongside the 'Engine' shaft.

The upcast and the Kitty shaft drew from the Busty seam at 1,038ft. and raised one-ton tubs instead of the old 12cwt. tubs. The Engine shaft drew from the Low Main inset at 498ft. and the John shaft drew from Bensham inset at 318ft., four shafts all in a line and all drawing coal. But within

Seghill Colliery 1920

three years the Kitty shaft lay idle and the ropes and the pulley wheels were removed.

A brickworks was also built alongside the Colliery. In all a grandiose scheme that proved all too ambitious. The Seghill royalty, although a small one, was blessed by having thick seams amongst the shallower measures. However when they reached the lower seams they found the 3/4, the Brockwell and the Victoria very thin.

They tried to overcome this disadvantage by the introduction of a method of mining that the director Walton Brown had seen employed in America. The method was called the skip method and involved first undercutting and firing the face. The coals were then pushed on to the conveyor by hauling a skip along the face. Although the men adapted well to these conditions the practice was later abandoned by the NCB after a miner was badly injured.

In 1949 the Kitty's shaft's headgear, which had stood since 1933, was dismantled by the NCB and moved to Bedlington F Colliery. The winder followed in 1953.

The Colliery survived to nationalisation, and was not in too bad a condition. Locomotives had been in use underground for several years. In 1954 the NCB installed skip winding in the Engine shaft and upgraded the washer.

By 1960 the John shaft was no longer drawing coal and the upcast shaft was being used only as a man-riding shaft. The Engine shaft remained as the only coal-drawing shaft. In 1961 the NCB transferred much of the Seghill reserves to Eccles Colliery — a sure sign that time was running out for this famous pit.

From its rich seams Seghill had produced 442,000 tons of coal a year and employed 1,300 men at the height of its productive capacity.

Seghill Colliery had developed an extensive sidings and rail network for the transportation of its product to the staithes at

British Jeffrey diamond coal cutter 1929 working at Seghill Colliery
Photograph Beamish Museum

Tippler House, Seghill

Seghill Colliery 1929

Howdon and to its other markets reached through the British Rail system.

On 28th September 1962 it was announced that the mine would close. The washery had an extended lease of life surviving the Colliery by several years, washing both opencast coal and that of other mines. The brickworks survived both the mine and the washery until it too was closed towards the end of 1977.

Seams worked at Seghill Colliery

1. High Main.
2. Main Coal (Grey Seam or Stone Coal).
3. Blake[1]
4. Yard.
5. Maudlin (Bensham).
6. Low Main (Five Quarter).
7. Brass Thill (Low Main).
8. Hutton (Plessey).
9. Harvey (Beaumont or Engine).
10. Tilley (Denton Low Main).
11. Top Busty.
12. Bottom Busty.
13. Three Quarter.
14. Brockwell.
15. Victoria.

Note

1 The Main Coal seam splits in this area and Seghill mine worked the Blake seam, which in other parts of the coalfield is known as the Top Yard seam. In one area of the mine the Grey and the Blake seams run together and are separated by only six inches. The two seams were worked as one giving an eight-feet-thick face. The Blake seam may have been called after a director of the Company.

Shilbottle and Whittle Collieries

The three seams of coal in the Shilbottle and Whittle area are the Townsend, Cannel and Shilbottle, which are part of the Middle Limestone Series. In this area of the coalfield the upper measures are missing because of erosion. Of these three seams only the Shilbottle is workable and is famous throughout the world for its quality as household coal.

The area constitutes an isolated island

Shilbottle Colliery in 1926

Whittle upcast shaft, 1986

on the eastern side of the coalfield; it is physically separated from the rest of the coalfield by the Great Whin Sill Dyke to the west and north, and to the south by the Hauxley Fault.

The Shilbottle seam outcrops to the west of Longframlington and dips eastwards where, just before Newton on the Moor, it hits a fault which throws the seam up 270 feet, causing it to outcrop again in the Whittle area before dipping eastwards.

Around 1917 the three principal mines in the area were Longframlington and Whittle Drift, both owned by the South Shilbottle Coal Company, and Shilbottle Colliery, which started its life as the Longdyke Pit and was owned by the Shilbottle Coal Company.

Isolated from the rest of the coalfield, and unique in that they only worked the one seam, peculiar to that area, they also distinguished themselves by achieving some unusual engineering feats.

There was an aerial ropeway from Longframlington colliery (map reference 81NU131021) to the screens at Whittle Colliery (81NU175065), a distance of over three miles. With its 35-feet-high pylons and six-horse-power engine, it was capable of transporting 32 tons per hour.

The company also constructed a three-and-a-half-mile endless top-rope haulage system. With two bridges, steep gradients and, at one point, a severe bend, it took the tubs from the Longdyke shaft to a coal depot on the NER line just outside of Alnwick.

Sometime before 1920 the Co-operative Wholesale Society (CWS) took over the Shilbottle Coal Company and the Longdyke pit, seeking to expand its operations. Longdyke's set-up was out of date and the sinking of a new colliery began in 1925. It had its own rail link, which was a branch line of just under two miles to the main London-to-Edinburgh line; the junction was one-and-a-half miles south of Alnmouth station.

The new sinking, the Grange Pit, known today as Shilbottle Colliery (map reference 81NY214080), had two shafts. The North, an upcast shaft, and the South, a coal-drawing shaft, were both 945ft. deep. Coal production began in 1926.

The CWS took over the South Shilbottle Coal Company in 1930. Having already closed Longdyke when Grange started drawing coal, it would also close Longframlington around 1931 and concentrate on mining the Shilbottle and Whittle Pits.

Shilbottle Colliery in 1986

The Company mainly worked its pits using 60-, 80- and 100-yard handfilling faces, moving the coal underground using pit ponies and both endless and main and tail rope haulage.

In 1947 the NCB brought investment and changes, not all of them believed to be for the better. From 1948 to 1952 Shilbottle colliery was transformed. Underground a three-mile straight roadway for locomotives was driven to allow the mine to work its seam on the horizontal mining system. This was a German method, in which all the coal is taken to one loading point and from there transported to the shafts.

The two shafts reversed roles with the old upcast now the coal-drawing shaft. The old coal shaft (South) now became the ventilation shaft with a new ventilation fan and fan drift. New screens were built for grading the coal.

At its peak Shilbottle produced 272,000

Longdyke Pit in 1912

Longdyke Pit, 1914
Photo George Nairn, Chester le Street

tons of coal a year and employed 807 men.

The Whittle Drift runs next to the A1 main road near the Newton on the Moor turn-off. The drift that the CWS took over in 1930 had been sunk in 1917 and was near to the present screens; a drift existed before that but its location is unknown. There are no records of when the small upcast shaft was sunk. It is possible that it was one of many that were dotted along the face of the outcrop in that area and utilised by the South Shilbottle company as an upcast for ventilation. The shaft is only 150ft. deep and has one small cage in it.

Under the NCB there were changes at the drift. After the success of the Shilbottle modernisation in the 1950s, it was decided Whittle would be next, and in 1965 a new drift was sunk about a mile and a half

Aerial ropeway, 1932

from the old one, at map reference 81NU174067. The drift was 500 metres long, dipping at a gradient of one in three, and was producing coal by 1966.

Whereas Shilbottle used locomotives to transport its coal, Whittle was belt-fed all the way to the drift entrance, where the coal was loaded into wagons and taken to the screens on a standard-gauge track.

There was also a narrow-gauge track for conveying the men from the pithead baths to the drift and for transporting materials. Whittle worked the seam in basically the same way as Shilbottle, with 60-, 80- and 100-yard handfilling faces, and under the NCB 120-yard faces were bottom cut, then fired and again handfilled.

In 1978 a roadway was driven from Shilbottle to Whittle Drift and the mines were merged. This decision was taken as the workings of both collieries were progressing in the same direction.

The inevitable decision was taken on 4th October 1982 and Shilbottle ceased production, the men being transferred to Whittle.

Some men said they left Shilbottle on the Friday and were back at the same coal face on Monday, the only difference being that they got there via Whittle.

Whittle Drift in 1986

With the 1982 merger of the pits and the new outlook of British Coal, it was decided to install 240-yard shearer faces, a decision that has been condemned as creating a disaster from the start. The official reason given by BC for announcing the closure of Whittle was that the seam had thinned to 28 inches and the smallest shearer drum on the market was a 34-inch drum available on the Eichoff machine. The shearer would therefore have been cutting six inches of stone and that would have seriously affected the vend. This, they argued, made the the mine unviable.

The men complained bitterly that for over 300 years the seam had been worked by hand, yet in a few years under British Coal the pit was lost.

At its peak Whittle Colliery produced over 700,000 tons a year. In 1982 the manpower rose to over 1,100 men with the influx of the Shilbottle men. This figure fell back to 800 within a few months. The mine was served by a branch over four miles long to the main London to Edinburgh line just north of Acklington station. Closure was announced in March 1987, and production ceased almost immediately.

Whittle Drift, however, is still working today as a private mine producing top-quality handfilled coal for the household market.

Throckley Isabella Colliery

The Throckley Coal Company was formed in 1867, with a Major Stephenson, a Mr Boyd, a Mr Simpson and a Mr John Spencer as the main directors. John Spencer owned the Newburn Steelworks.

The company began sinking two shafts in that year on the southern outskirts of Throckley, not far from the river Tyne (map reference 88NZ153668).

The mine and main coal-drawing shaft,

The Isabella upcast and Derwentwater shaft in 1900
Photograph West Newcastle Local Studies

Air-powered cutting machine of the type used at the Isabella

The Derwentwater shaft prior to demolition, 1938 Photograph Charlton Thompson, Durham

the Isabella, took their name from one of the director's wives.

The shafts were both sunk to the Brockwell seam at 336ft., though the upcast went down a few fathoms more to make a sump for pumping.

A few years later a third shaft, the Derwentwater, was sunk to Brockwell seam. Though it did draw coal for a short while, its main use was for pumping. The shaft had a massive steam pump that was capable of pumping 2,500 gallons per minute.

The water was collected in a sump just below the surface and then taken along an 'addit' (an underground drainage tunnel) to the nearby Reigh burn.

The steam pump was later replaced by electric pumps of 2,000 gallons per minute capacity.

The Derwentwater headgears were pulled down in 1940, and by 1955 water was such a problem from the now-closed mine that a submersible pump had to be put into the old Derwentwater shaft.

The Isabella was plagued by the ever-present hazard of unmarked old workings; a problem which is endemic in a much-worked and ancient coalfield.

Charlton Thompson, a surface official at the Colliery, remembers the discovery in 1950 of two old shafts at the Isabella when the surface of the pit yard collapsed.

On another occasion, when the old Glybal Fan was replaced by a 30ft. diameter waddle fan, a fan drift was driven. This ended up in the same position as an old shaft, which collapsed, taking the fan drift with it. The mine had to revert to the old

Dismantling the Derwentwater shaft in 1940. A young Charlton Thompson sits on the beam Photograph Charlton Thompson, Durham

Throckley Isabella Colliery, 1953 Photograph West Newcastle Local Studies

fan to keep going. The two old shafts were later found to go down to the Main Coal seam at about 240-270 feet.

The Isabella had little mechanisation, not having conveyors until 1945. Even under the NCB there was little improvement.

The mine's output was over 70,000 tons a year from 345 men.

The Isabella had a one-and-a-half-mile branch rail line via the screens at Lemington.

Production stopped at Isabella on 29th January 1954, with the seams all but exhausted. Today the site is a nature reserve with some of main buildings still standing.

Seams worked at Throckley Isabella Colliery

1. **Plessey (Ruler).**
2. **Harvey (Engine Townley or Beaumont).**
3. **Hodge.**
4. **Tilley (Splint).**
5. **Busty (Stone).**
6. **Top Busty (Main Coal).**
7. **Bottom Busty (Low Main).**
8. **3/4 (3/4 Yard or 5/4).**
9. **Brockwell (Bandy).**
10. **Victoria.**

Wallsend Rising Sun Colliery

The Wallsend Rising Sun Colliery was an extension of the old Wallsend Colliery, which was sunk in 1784 and whose principal shafts were the G shaft and the Edward pit.

In 1850 a dispute arose between the owners of the Friars Goose pumping engine, in Felling, and all the mine owners in Tyne basin over sharing the costs of keeping the mines free of water. As the mine owners refused to pay, the pumping operation was stopped and the pits of Wallsend and Hebburn were inundated.

This act of criminal stupidity could well

Wallsend G Colliery in 1910, showing massive pumping beam over H Pit
Photograph Peter Martin, Blaydon

Wallsend G Colliery after modernisation Photograph Beamish Museum

have been the origin of the Victorian adage 'Penny wise, pound foolish', as the cost of rectifying this mistake was colossal.

In 1863 the Tyne Coal Company was formed to reopen the drowned-out pits, and was able to secure £60,000 capital through an act of Parliament to assist them in this venture.

The company planned to sink a new shaft, the H Pit, 30 yards south east of the existing G Pit, which stood at map reference 88NZ311664.

This work began on 9th August 1866, with the aid of two giant Cornish-type pumping engines, which were built by Andrew Barclay Limited of Kilmarnock and had a joint capacity of 5,000 gallons per minute.

Two years later in 1868 the water level in the G Pit was down to 330ft., with a corresponding reduction in the level of water in the entire royalty, including Friars Goose.

By 1870 Hebburn Colliery on the Durham side of the Tyne was drained to the Low Main seam at 1,020ft. proving that this pit had no direct underground connection with the other mines in the area.

Hebburn began drawing coal in the September of that year.

By 1873, now a full seven years after this ambitious operation began, they had only reduced the the level of the water in the H Pit to 320ft. and the G shaft to 350ft., a reduction of only 20ft. from the 1868 level.

Understandably, by 1891 the Tyne Company was in financial difficulties and was dissolved. A new company, the Wallsend and Hebburn Coal Company, took over the operations.

The new company aimed to continue with the sinking of the H shaft and to reopen the G Pit. George Baker Forster, who had been the viewer for the Cowpen Coal Company and had taken charge of the rescue work in the Hartley disaster, took over control of the work.

By 16th August 1891 the H Pit was 72 feet below the Bensham seam and started to draw coal from the Yard seam.

In 1901 work began in the Low Main and Bensham seams from the G Pit.

The company, however, were having problems pumping out the northern side of the royalty over a mile from the G Pit shaft, where beyond the old workings the water was at a pressure of 180lbs per

The new washer at Rising Sun, 1936

No. 2 upcast shaft and washer at Rising Sun Colliery in the 1950s

square inch. This caused a great deal of concern until it was brought under control.

To add to their difficulties the mine developed a gas problem and, to overcome this and to reduce the distance of the workings from the shaft, a new shaft was sunk on the edge of the royalty at the Rising Sun Farm (map reference 88NZ232877).

This work began on 21st February 1906 and the Bensham seam was reached at 768ft. on 18th February 1908.

As the new Rising Sun workings moved further from the G shaft, which still ventilated the mine, the need for a another shaft became clear and No. 2 shaft was started in 1912. It reached the Bensham seam on 27th August 1915, making Rising Sun Colliery independent of G Pit.

In 1913 the old Edward shaft was opened for coal drawing.

The No. 1 shaft had an electric winder fitted in 1922, the No. 2 shaft already having one.

In the 1920s G Pit was totally rebuilt and a staple pit was sunk in 1928 at the Rising Sun between the Bensham and Beaumont seams. The shaft was 13 feet in diameter and had a 150-horsepower winder with double-deck cages.

The huge cost of pumping and the effects of the great depression forced the closure of the Edward Pit in 1932, one year before Hebburn Colliery closed. The H and G shafts followed in 1934.

The G Pit opened and closed as the market dictated.

By late 1934 the Rising Sun was the only mine left open when the the Wallsend and Hebburn Coal Company was taken over by the Bedlington Coal Company.

A redevelopment of the Rising Sun was undertaken by the new company: underground haulage was changed, all steam plant was removed, and a new surface washery was built capable of processing 160 tons of coal per hour.

The No. 2 upcast shaft was deepened to the Brockwell seam at 1,296ft., with insets at the Main Coal and Beaumont seams, all for coal drawing.

A second staple pit, this time a drop shaft[1], was added in 1938 between the Main Coal and Bensham seams near to the No. 1 shaft.

In 1940 the company installed two large double-deck cages with three tubs per deck in the No. 2 shaft to take coal from the newly-entered 3/4 seam.

By the outbreak of the Second World War the Rising Sun was a well-equipped modern mine, by far the most productive of the group.

In 1954, seven years after nationalisation, 90 per cent of the Colliery's reserves were in the lower measures and, as the No. 1 shaft did not reach these seams, coal drawing depended on the staple pits. By this time the No. 2 shaft (upcast) was being more and more used for coal drawing.

In 1955 No. 3 shaft was sunk to the Brockwell seam with an inset at the Beaumont seam. The shaft was 20 feet in diameter and 1,300ft. deep, the second deepest in Northumberland. This shaft was fitted with an Asea multi-friction rope-winding tower of Swedish design, one of only two in the country, the other being

1 I.e. the coal was dropped down the shaft, which was fitted with a spiral chute.

The new No. 3 and old No. 1 coal shafts. No. 3 is on the left

at Weetslade Colliery. The mine could now draw coal from either seam at any time, or from both at once. The old No. 1 shaft then became idle and No. 2 was used for man-riding only.

A complex system of underground locomotives took the coal from the districts to the new shaft.

It was planned to make Rising Sun a 500,000-plus mine, a target it was to meet with some ease.

The Rising Sun had a one-and-a-quarter mile branch rail line to the British Rail system. The coal was transported by BR to the straithes, where it was exported.

At its peak the pit produced over 550,000 tons of coal per annum and employed 1,750 men.

The cheap oil policy of the 1960s certainly had its effect on the profitability of the Rising Sun Colliery, but in the end it was the old enemy, the water, that won. For every ton of coal that was drawn seven tons of water were pumped out of the Colliery. The problem was compounded by the Colliery's position— it was the last colliery south of the 90 Fathom Dyke. This meant that the huge burden of the pumping costs could not be shared by other collieries, as was the practice where several collieries benefited from a single pumping operation.

The NCB declared the pit unviable and the Rising Sun closed on 26th April 1969. Many men left the industry; others uprooted their families and moved south, creating their own Geordie village in Nottinghamshire.

Seams worked at Wallsend Rising Sun Colliery

1. High Main.
2. Main Coal (Metal).
3. Yard.
4. Maudlin (Bensham).
5. Low Main (which split in the Wallsend area to become 5/4 and 6/4 seams).
6. Brass Thill (Low Main).
7. Hutton (Plessey).
8. Harvey (Beaumont).
9. 3/4 (3/4 Main).
10. Brockwell.

It is possible that after 1947 some coal was worked from the Edward and G Pits, but by 1950 they were no more than pumping shafts.

No. 3 shaft and washer at Rising Sun Colliery, 1968

Woodhorn Colliery 1920

Woodhorn Colliery

Woodhorn Colliery was the third pit to be sunk by the Ashington Coal Company. The Company sank the first shaft, the No. 1 shaft, on the outskirts of Woodhorn (map reference 81NZ289884), nearly two miles east of Ashington. Work began on 16th May 1894.

The No. 1 downcast shaft, the first of the colliery's two shafts, was sunk to the Plessey Seam at 873ft. However when it first drew coal, in February 1898, it did so from an inset at the Yard seam level, at 570ft.

The No. 2, the upcast shaft, was also sunk to the Plessey at 888ft., but drew its first coals in 1901 from the Low Main seam by way of a shaft inset at 780ft.

The Ashington Coal Company created an extensive, well-mechanised mine, installing coal cutters in 1903. Coal was transported underground by endless rope haulers, while pit ponies were used to take supplies in bye.

Tragically in 1902 two men were killed at the Colliery in a gas explosion.

Filling tub off belt

Woodhorn Colliery 1978

On 13th August 1916 disaster struck again when in another gas explosion 13 lives were lost: eight deputies, three stonemen and two putters.

Many more lives would have been lost but for the fact that the explosion occurred during the course of a Sunday night maintenance shift.

A memorial cross was erected in Hirst Park for the victims of the explosion. This cross can now be seen at the Colliery as part of the Woodhorn Colliery Museum.

In 1941 the Pit survived a direct hit by a German bomb that demolished the Fan House. Mercifully no lives were lost and even production was not affected because of the existence of an emergency fan.

Under NCB management the Colliery continued to prosper, producing coal from 220-yard shearer faces and employing battery-driven locomotives to transport the coal to the shafts.

The close proximity of Ashington and Woodhorn Collieries allowed them to share a single washer. For this reason Woodhorn never had its own but transported its coal via a one-and-three-quarter mile link to Ashington where it was washed.

The streamlining of the Ashington and Woodhorn Collieries in the 1960s connected them underground and both drew their coal by way of the newly driven Bothal Drift at Ashington.

When the rationalisation programme was complete, the screens at Woodhorn were demolished and the Colliery began to take on a somewhat neglected look. In 1975 the NCB replaced the old steam winding engine with an electric winder, which had been salvaged from the recently closed Fenwick Colliery. This was to mark the end of steam winding in the Northumberland coalfield.

Throughout the 1970s the Colliery was confined to the lower and thinner seams. Production and manpower fell steadily throughout the 1970s and by the time closure came the manpower was down to 500 men. At its peak Woodhorn Colliery had produced 600,000 tons of coal a year and employed a little under 2,000 men.

Production at Woodhorn ended on 28th February 1981, with many men leaving the industry forever.

The head gear and surface buildings remain in place and are maintained as a mining museum. All aspects of Colliery life are on display, admission is free, and it is well worth a visit.

Woodhorn Colliery 1932 Photograph Norman Bell, Blyth

Woodhorn Colliery 1967. Screens are all but demolished

Seams worked at Woodhorn Colliery

1. Ashington D/E (This seam is often called the Blackclose or the Moorland).
2. High Main E (High Main).
3. High Main E2 (Diamond).
4. Main Coal F1 (Main Coal).
5. Main Coal F2 (Bottom Main).
6. Yard G1 (Top Yard or Bentink).
7. Yard G2 (Yard).
8. Low Main (Five Quarter).
9. Brass Thill (Low Main).
10. Hutton L (Plessey or Top Plessey).
11. Plessey M (Bottom Plessey).

It has not been possible to find any records of Woodhorn Colliery working the Maudlin Seam (Bensham) or any of the low seams. It is probable that the Maudlin split in this area and was left in favour of the Five Quarter. The lower seams were probably all worked from Ashington.

Sources

1. The Guide to the Coalfields (various years).
2. The Chronological Records of Coal Mining Transport in Northumberland and Durham from 1180 to 1839, by George Lister.
3. The Colliery Year Book and Directory 1947-1975.
4. The Colliery Guardian 1880 to 1975.
5. The Colliery Engineers 1928 to 1966
6. Strata of Northumberland and Durham.
7. Borings and Sinkings — North of England Institute of Mining and Mechanical Engineers 1860-1978.
8. Reeds Guide to the Coalfields (various volumes).
9. The Transactions of the North of England Institute of Mining and Mechanical Engineers 1860-1978.
10. The National Association of Colliery Managers Transactions 1900-1950.
11. The History of Blackhill Colliery, a synopsis by Ron Hope.
12. The NCB abandoned seams plans, County Records Office.
13. Views of the Collieries by T.H. Hair.
14. The Iron Steel and Coal Review, 1942 to 1968.
15. Coal Mining: a Technological Chronology 1700 to 1950, by Alan Hill
16. The records of the County Records Office at Meldon Park and Morpeth.
17. The sinking of the Newbiggin colliery —Transactions of the North of England Institute of Mining and Mechanical Engineers.
18. The documents records and memories of the late L.G. Charlton.
19. The archives of Beamish Museum.
20. The History of the Parish of Wallsend, by William Richardson (1923).
21. The miners of Northumberland, their memories and recollections.

A young Andrew Tyler with carbide lamp. He is now a 73-year-old grandfather